AHEAD OF TIME

AHEAD
OF TIME

EDITED BY

Harry Harrison and
Theodore J. Gordon

DOUBLEDAY & COMPANY, INC.
GARDEN CITY, NEW YORK

1972

ACKNOWLEDGMENTS

Grateful acknowledgment is made to the following for permission to reprint the articles included in this book:

"The Conquest of Senescence" by Robert W. Prehoda. Reprinted by permission of the author.

"People Freezing: The Establishment Thaws" by R. C. W. Ettinger. Copyright © 1971 by R. C. W. Ettinger. Reprinted by permission of the author.

"What Are Tachyons, and What Could We Do with Them?" by Gerald Feinberg. Reprinted by permission of the author.

"Inside-out Worlds" by Dandridge M. Cole and Donald W. Cox, first published in *Islands in Space* by Dandridge M. Cole and Donald W. Cox. Copyright © 1964 by Dandridge M. Cole and Donald W. Cox. Reprinted by permission of the Chilton Book Company, Philadelphia.

"Requirements for Communications to a Naive Recipient" by Albert G. Wilson and Theodore J. Gordon. Reprinted by permission of the authors.

"Search for Artificial Stellar Sources of Infrared Radiation" by Freeman J. Dyson, first published in *Science,* Volume 131, 1960. Reprinted by permission of the author.

"Psychology in the Year 2000" by Gardner Murphy, first published in *American Psychologist,* May 1969. Copyright © 1969 by the American Psychological Association, Inc., and reprinted by their permission.

"Do Plants Feel Emotions?" by Thorn Bacon and Richard Kirkpatrick, first published in *National Wildlife,* February–March 1969. Reprinted by permission of *National Wildlife,* Milwaukee, Wisconsin.

"Anomalous Prediction of Quantum Processes by Some Human Subjects" by Helmut Schmidt. Reprinted by permission of the author.

"Long Delayed Echoes of Radio Transmissions" by O. G. Villard, Jr., C. R. Graf, and J. M. Lomasney, first published in *QST,* May 1969. Reprinted by permission of the American Radio Relay League, Inc.

"The Life and Death of Project Camelot" by Irving L. Horowitz. Copyright © 1965 by *TRANS-action* Magazine, New Brunswick, New Jersey. Reprinted by permission of *TRANS-action.*

"The Jousting at Camelot—or Social Technology Encounters the Shield of the Social Structure" by Theodore R. Vallance. Copyright © 1971 by Theodore R. Vallance. Reprinted by permission of the author.

"Ovshinsky: Promoter or Persecuted Genius?" by P. M. Boffey, first published in *Science,* Volume 165, August 1969. Copyright © 1969 by

CONTENTS

INTRODUCTION

A new idea is a rare and peculiar kind of perception. It is a commodity which can be bought and sold, stolen, or given without cost. Like all knowledge, its transfer adds to the intellectual inventory of the receiver, but without diminishing that of the giver. No one is sure about its physical form: Perhaps it is a conjunction of neurons carrying a complex series of electrical impulses in the convoluted recesses of the cortex, or perhaps it is an intricate series of proteins and amino acids deployed in precise and delicate relationship along a strand of DNA. Some hedonists say that it can be stimulated with drugs; some psychologists court it with fresh air, good lighting, and a healthy digestion. Whatever its commercial form, wherever it lies within the brain, no matter how it is cajoled and coaxed into being, a new idea is a relatively rare occurrence, a confluence of electrochemical and social improbabilities that few people have ever experienced.

This is a book about new ideas.

New ideas have some disconcerting properties. First of all, most of them are wrong, for all time and irrevocably. Perhaps this is because there are so many ways to be wrong and so few to be right.

Secondly, new ideas may get their originators into a great deal of trouble. An innovator who presents a brilliant new idea which somehow challenges the dogma of the day may meet laughter, incredulity, derision, and persecution. This was true in the past and can still be true today, despite our reverence and need for change. The forms of persecution used against innovators whose ideas are out of phase with their discipline may have changed over the past centuries, but the persecution is just as real; our burnings-at-the-stake are figurative but just as effective. Innovators have lost their jobs, as well as their security clearances (which may be worse). Means of normal scientific communication have been closed to them; they have been refused publication space; legal action has been taken to prevent them from lecturing. Sometimes their work may be stamped with cautionary labels added by editors, thus rejecting them by innuendo. Funding may be difficult or impossible to obtain.

There are many examples of such treatment in the history of science, religion, and politics. The list is already well worn: Socrates, Galileo, Maxwell, Mendel, and Ampere are a few who faced their peers with new ideas and were judged irresponsible. Some, like Bruno and Servetus, were murdered; Semmelweis and Wells went insane proclaiming the truth of their ideas. Yet their ideas and those of others similarly treated now occupy lofty positions in the hardy framework of dogma, waiting for the kind of challenge they themselves once offered.

Thomas Kuhn, in his brilliant book, *The Structure of Scientific Revolutions,* studied the flow of scientific history. He found it not a continuous stream, each new idea adding its energy to ever-widening disciplines, but rather a discontinuous series of crises. In his image, the business of normal science is the probing of the limits of the accepted paradigms, the laws and theories that comprise the content of the disciplines. Most scientists do this kind of work most of the time, adding precision to known consistencies, testing the applicability of accepted concepts in new environments. Belief in these paradigms is a requirement of the guild; students are taught these, and when they know them by rote, are graduated.

But occasionally the old beliefs fail in new circumstances. Phlogiston, phrenology, caloric are among the debris of advancing science. Kuhn calls the trauma which results in the rejection of accepted theories and their replacement with others "the crises of science." Crises are times of trial. Old ideas cannot be lightly discarded; careers are built on them, and reputations sometimes rest on their continued acceptance. When old ideas are discarded, part of the firmament disappears; the textbooks are wrong; honored professors, false. Every premise of the discipline must be re-examined and the pieces put back together with some semblance of order, hopefully greater than that which existed before.

At a time of scientific crisis new ideas are welcome, according to Kuhn. At other times the discipline is simply not ready for concepts which lie outside its accepted bounds; science is being conducted well enough, according to old principles. Even in time of crisis some scientists reject new ideas, clinging to the concepts which guided them so well in the past.

Out of this image comes the conclusion that there must be a class of new ideas and concepts in existence today which have been rejected for purely epistemological reasons. (Other conclusions are probably equally important—for example, that the organization of science is not conducive to radical innovation—but these are the subjects of other prospective essays.) If such ideas are casting about, some of them must surely be simply ahead of their time, and when crises occur, will be suddenly remembered, and will become good science, rationalized into acceptability.

This book is an attempt to collect papers dealing with ideas that may later be judged to have been ahead of their time. Some of the papers deal with new ideas themselves; these are straightforward presentations of new concepts which stretch the frontiers of accepted disciplines. For example, Gerald Feinberg, a physicist at Columbia University, has contributed a paper describing the tachyon, a theoretical particle moving faster than the speed of light, and the uses that some future society might make of such a particle.

Another group of papers deals with the reaction to new ideas in areas of current controversy or uncertainty. These papers, drawn from different specialties, testify that the sociology of science sometimes mimics evolutionary selection, and reinforces the accepted and "official" directions of current inquiry. In this catagory, R. C. W. Ettinger has written about the status of the body-freezing movement and Robert Prehoda discusses the politics of research into the causes and cures of aging.

Finally, a third group of papers contains suggestions for future research which might well open new horizons to science. Here for example, Gardner Murphy permitted us to include his insightful discussion about the shape of psychology in the year 2000.

As editors we wish that we could give the reader positive assurance that these invited papers and reprinted articles comprehensively cover these three domains. But we cannot say that we have done more than sample important new ideas, important scientific controversies, and important directions of research and disciplinary change. Our own taxonomy and the nature of the problem determined our own incompleteness.

The subject matter of these papers ranges from feeling in plants to conflicts in sociology, from communications with extra-terrestrials to the molecular structure of water. Some are undoubtedly inspired glimpses into nature as it will be understood in the next century. Others will deservedly wither.

But who among us can now judge with certainty which is which?

AHEAD OF TIME

1

R. W. PREHODA

The Conquest of
Senescence

*Medical research has been directed toward the elimination of
suffering through the amelioration of disease. As one disease
after another is controlled in a society, as infant mortality is
further diminished, life expectancy at birth has grown until it
finally has approached a plateau. In the United States, for
example, life expectancy at birth grew from forty-nine years in
1900 to sixty-four years in 1940. Since that time it has improved
only to about seventy years. This plateau probably will be un-
assailable until more insight is gained into the aging process itself.*

*Old age is the final state of existence that is waiting for us all
if we manage to survive encounters with accidents and disease.
In view of our reverence of sex and youth, it is surprising
that we have not put more effort into aging research. In the
following article, Mr. Prehoda, authority on gerentology and
author of* Extended Youth, *surveys the aging research now being
conducted and the sociology of the bureaus responsible for
funding or not funding this work. He forecasts some paths this
work might take, given adequate insight, patience, and funds,
and describes a proposal for reversing the process.*

Our earliest written records demonstrate that man has always sought to extend his life-span and youthful vitality. One early Egyptian papyrus details a rejuvenation formula including such dubious ingredients as crocodile blood and sandlewood oil which would . . . "return strength to both arms and loins." Ponce de Leon looked for the "fountain of youth" while contemporary alchemists searched for the elusive "elixir of life" which would return youth to the aged.

Legends of long-lived ancestors are common to all cultures. The Book of Genesis accords Methuselah a life-span of 969 years, and six of the other antediluvian (before the flood) patriarchs are given life-spans in excess of nine hundred years. In 1780, Benjamin Franklin predicted that "all disease may be by sure means prevented or cured not excepting that of Old Age, and our lives lengthened at pleasure even beyond the antediluvian standard."

Control of infectious diseases has brought the average American life-span up to the Biblical "three score and ten," but any significant extension beyond seventy years requires that the fundamental causes of biological aging be understood and modified. The new science of gerontology is tackling this goal and in the past few years an increasingly clear picture of the causes of aging has emerged. Means to control biological senescence may very well prove to be the most significant scientific breakthrough of this century. If the requisite funding is made available, many readers may have their life-spans doubled or even tripled.

Gerontologists have suggested many theories of aging, but we now appear to be narrowing the list down to several of the more probable causes of mammalian senescence. Each aging theory is usually accompanied by some proposed means of correction, offering the hope of a significant reduction in the rate of adverse biological change. Moreover, it now appears that all of the leading explanations of aging can be tied together into a composite theory allowing senescence to be completely understood. Past experience in science shows that full understanding of physical and biological phenomena has usually been followed by practical means of control.

The Cross-Linkage Theory has been refined during the past thirty years by Dr. Johan Bjorksten, founder of the Bjorksten Research Laboratories, in Madison, Wisconsin. This theory is based on molecular changes within and around all the cells of the body. Bjorksten holds that aging is caused by a gradual, but progressive, chemical cross-linkage of large vital protein and nucleic acid molecules. Most of the random cross-linkages are harmless, since the various enzymes within the body can break them apart. However, a certain percentage are cross-linked in a manner which prevents natural body enzymes from splitting these bound-together molecules which can no longer function normally. As this process continues, the vital proteins and nucleic acid molecules are bound together in pairs, and even larger aggregates, which are irreversibly immobilized. The resulting accumulation of this "frozen metabolic pool" clogs the cells, interferes with the functioning of the remaining free molecules, and ultimately destroys the cells.

The body contains many agents which cause molecular cross-linking. Some are intermediate products which accumulate in the body when more food is taken in than can be immediately utilized. Ionizing radiation forms free radicals which are very powerful cross-linking agents. Tobacco smoke and smog also cause an accumulation of cross-linking agents. The molecules of life are in the shape of long chains or spiral forms, and the cross-linking agents act like little rods with two hooks which link together two giant molecules.

The Swiss gerontologist Dr. Frederic Verzar and a number of other investigators have proved conclusively that *collagen*, the protein which constitutes 40 per cent of all of the protein in the body, becomes progressively cross-linked as animals and humans age. There is also conclusive experimental evidence of cross-linking in DNA and other vital body proteins. Collagen is important because it supplies the matrix in which are deposited the calcium salts which give the bones their hardness.

Collagen is the substance of cartilage and tendon; it fills the space between muscle fibers and between the cells of many organs, serving as the stabilizing fiber of connective tissue. Collagen is the principal constituent of the skin which so graphically mirrors progressive aging. Even if cross-linking affected only collagen, it would play an important role in the aging process.

Dr. Bjorksten has proposed a possible therapy which would control and, within limits, permit some degree of rejuvenation. He would break down all of the cross-linked molecule groups so that they could be excreted from the cells, thereby freeing the space they occupied for synthesis of new normal molecules. This might be accomplished by an elastase or some enzyme already known. Soil bacteria are certain to contain suitable enzymes, since the earth is not covered with deposits of cross-linked protein. The proper soil bacteria enzymes should be obtained by starting with cross-linked protein taken from the organs of old animals, breaking it down as far as we can with known enzymes, washing out and digesting out of it all soluble material and making the remaining hard-core substances the only nitrogen source in a mixed culture of soil microorganisms. Only organisms capable of breaking down the cross-linked material could then survive. A number of such bacteria are likely to be found. These different organisms could be grown in quantity, the enzymes extracted, and out of many thousands of soil bacteria strains, an enzyme-rejuvenating "elixir" might be found.

It would not be necessary for the suitable enzymes to break the cross-linkage themselves; it would be equally effective to break down the cross-linked molecules in a way which would reduce them to small, excretable fragments. If the enzymes also attacked normal proteins, they could be administered at such a slow rate that the normal synthesis in the cell would replace all that was being broken down. This could be stimulated by administering suitable hormones, permitting the normal protein and nucleic acids to be replaced. The restoration of all the cells to a more active state would rejuvenate the organism.

During the last few years Dr. Bjorksten has led a well-funded scientific team engaged in the pursuit of soil bacteria enzymes that can slow down or reverse aging changes caused by cross-linking. Results to date are very encouraging, and I will venture the prediction that a youth extending "elixir" may be available to the public within the next ten years. Enzyme treatments would probably involve self-administered injections in a pattern similar to that followed by diabetics. Additional evidence of the role of cross-linking in aging is also coming from many laboratories, and some leading scientists, including Nobel prize winners, now conclude that Bjorksten's theory accounts for the major cause of human senescence.

The Free Radical Theory—proposed by Dr. Denham Harman of the University of Nebraska—partly explains aging as being caused by the harmful side effects of free radicals (extremely active chemical substances) which are produced in the course of normal metabolism, and by oxidation of the connective tissue by molecular oxygen. The free radicals probably initiate degenerative changes primarily by removing hydrogen atoms from biologically vital cellular constituents such as DNA. Free radicals are also the most powerful cross-linking agents in the body.

Dr. Harman is conducting experiments employing chemicals which neutralize free radicals before they can react with the vital molecules in the tissues. These chemicals, called antioxidants, were originally developed to minimize radiation damage which is partly caused by free radical formation.

One antioxidant, BHT (butylated hydroxytoluene), was able to increase the half survival time (age at which 50 per cent are dead) of mice by 50.3 per cent over the controls. This would be equivalent to increasing the average human life-span from 70 years to 105 years. Another antioxide, santoquin, increased the half survival time of mice by 71.7 per cent—equivalent to an average life-span of 120 years! Their experiments are not conclusive, however, because the controls did not live as long as they normally do, which seemed to be the result of synthetic food fed to all the mice.

Dr. Harman now has experiments under way that should correct the dietary deficiencies and provide conclusive evidence of the anti-aging effects of antioxidants. His research is extremely important because it promises to provide the first effective anti-aging therapy that could easily be taken in pill form by the general public. Vitamin E, Vitamin C, and the element selenium may also be important life-extending antioxidants.

The Stress Theory proposed by Dr. Hans Selye of the University of Montreal explains aging as an overreaction by certain glands to temperature change, bacterial infection, injury, and psychological trauma. He contends that a stressful situation will damage the organism, and a good rest will almost, but not quite, return the organism to its pre-stress condition. The stress theory can explain degenerative diseases that tend to accompany senescence, but animal experiments do not indicate that stress by itself causes aging. Quite probably stress acts to speed up the rate of other aging causes such as cross-linking, and also is an important factor in terminal illness when aging reduces the organism's ability to tolerate stress.

The Somatic Mutation Theory is most closely identified with Dr. Howard J. Curtis of the Brookhaven National Laboratory. Somatic cells are those responsible for maintenance of the organ in contrast to the germ cells—sperm and ova—which allow reproduction. Somatic mutations appear to be caused by changes in DNA (deoxyribonucleic acid) molecules within the nuclei of body cells. Thousands of DNA molecules are found in the forty-six chromosomes of each human somatic cell. The DNA molecules create several different kinds of RNA (ribonucleic acid) molecules, and by a process still not completely understood, the various forms of RNA are able to produce all of the substances which make up the tissues of the body.

In other words, a somatic mutation is some form of alteration in a DNA molecule that causes it to produce faulty RNA, which in turn can no longer synthesize the hormone, enzyme, or protein that is the end product of cell activity. A somatic mutation might also include damage that would prevent DNA from producing any RNA at all.

Many somatic mutations appear to be caused by cross-linking, which should be corrected by Bjorksten's proposed enzyme therapy. Dr. Curtis has proposed that other causes of somatic mutations may be corrected by augmenting natural processes within cells which repair damaged chromosomes. A more distant possibility is the creation of artificial viruses which would inject corrective DNA or RNA into aging cells.

The Immunological Theory emerged because it appears that the number of somatic mutations in the cells is inadequate to explain aging. During a normal lifetime, about 20 per cent of the body's cells undergo spontaneous mutation and to some extent become strangers within the organism. The body sets up an allergic reaction to foreign cells, the transplant immunity, which has been dramatized in heart replacement operations. Dr. Roy L. Walford of UCLA believes that these changed cells provoke the body's immunological defense system into producing antibodies against them. Since the mutated cells would still be similar to their unmutated sister cells, these antibodies would also attack the normal cells. There would be a random mutation process occurring in cells throughout the body, so this immunological attack would be against all the vital organs and less important tissues. As more mutations occur, the intensity of the allergic reaction would increase, causing a progressive degeneration throughout the body.

Dr. Walford has increased the life-span of mice 10 per cent by giving them Imuran, a drug which suppresses the immunologic system. He also points out that cross-linkages can cause somatic mutations, in turn leading to adverse immunologic changes. Walford also suggests that antibodies may be ideal cross-linking agents. No doubt immunologic changes contribute to aging, and this may be corrected by modification of early steps in the biological sequence of events such as cross-linking, and also by the much more sophisticated control of the immunologic system that can be expected from the great effort directed to organ transplantation.

A *Molecular-Genetic Theory* of aging is the most recent contribution of Dr. Bernard L. Strehler of the University of Southern California. Our cells are genetically programed to differentiate and become brain cells, liver cells, kidney cells, etc. All the cells of the body contain the same forty-six chromosomes which in turn have genes composed of DNA. Cells become specialized components of particular organs and tissues by a complex mechanism of selective gene activation and repression during the early stages of life and continuing through sexual maturity. Dr. Strehler suggests that this genetic repression may develop into a harmful pattern of adverse changes in aging cells, in which the DNA molecules cannot produce the correct RNA molecules which in turn must produce the enzymes and other vital components of tissues. His theory is based on our new understanding of the way amino acids are coded in DNA, and the complex "message translation" related to the genetic code and the sequence which culminates in the production of vital molecules—thus a "molecular-genetic theory."

Dr. Strehler has conducted preliminary radioisotope experiments with mice which seem to support his theory. He is optimistic that a way can be found to correct the changes leading to faulty "message translation" at the molecular level.

The Cybernetic Theory of aging is proposed by Dr. Joseph W. Still who contends that aging is caused by increased reaction time in all nervous and biochemical functions which in turn cause increased transmission time in those brain centers controlling the nervous-endocrine system. Aging is viewed as a gradual loss of control or coordination between all the cells in the body. Dr. Still points out that the organism may be dead, as in electrocution, and yet for a few minutes none of the vital cells is dead.

Dr. Still believes that the increased reaction time in the brain cells may be the result of "chemical stiffening" caused by cross-linking. He has conducted experiments using radioisotopes that support this explanation. All of the other explanations of aging seem to be compatible with the cybernetic theory which may be viewed as a framework within which the other theories act as functional blocks.

The Integrated Theory of Aging. The scientists proposing alternate aging theories bring to mind the classic story of the seven blind men examining an elephant—to the one feeling a leg, an elephant was like a tree; the one feeling the trunk thought he was like a big snake; etc.—each being correct so far as he went. Major Donald G. Carpenter of the U. S. Air Force Academy has attempted to combine the preceding aging models into an integrated theory of aging which offers the beginning of a true picture of the aging mechanism "elephant." The theory is subject to change as it is admittedly incomplete. For instance, Dr. Strehler's molecular-genetic theory is not yet included, but Dr. Carpenter appears to be close to the goal of a complete elucidation of senescence.

In the integrated theory, cross-linking of all types of molecules (not just proteins, enzymes, DNA, and RNA) is assumed to be the major cause of aging. The rate of cross-linkage is increased when the organism is subject to stress (chemical changes in the system are responsible). The cross-linked molecules are divided into two groups—genetic and non-genetic. The cross-linking of collagen and similar non-genetic molecules would affect the organism's total molecular efficiency, causing it to decrease. The diffusion of oxygen, hormones, and nutrients into the cells, and excretion of waste products would be hindered. The total molecular efficiency would also be decreased by the accumulation of waste products not caused by cross-linkage.

The cross-linkage of DNA produces somatic mutations, but mutations are also produced by other causes. The effect of the mutation is amplified by immunologic reactions, which are, in turn, increased by distortions in the control or system feedback between the central nervous system and the endocrine glands (cybernetic theory).

Cross-linkages, mutations, immunologic reactions, and cybernetic considerations (loss of control) acting together reduce the minimum efficiency of the sum total of the body's molecules required for survival. The minimum level becomes higher as the number of cross-linkages and mutations increases. The difference between the organism's total molecular efficiency and the minimum required for survival is a measure of the organism's ability to withstand stress. Whenever the stress encountered exceeds the organism's ability to withstand the stress, the organism dies.

Figure 1 presents a schematic view of the integrated theory of aging. This is a highly simplified picture and does not cover every detail. For instance, immunologic changes may cause additional cross-linkages, which, in turn, could accelerate the entire pattern of progressive decay. Somatic mutations could halt the production of intracellular enzymes which normally break apart cross-linked molecules.

Cellular Replacement is my proposed therapy to partly correct adverse age changes which may be caused by any combination of the preceding theories. A large percentage of non-dividing cells in vital organs such as the heart and brain die by the time a human reaches old age, and the other cells are not functioning properly. What is needed is a new supply or *replacement* of youthful cells into the aging body. Cellular replacement would require that the cells be taken from an "identical twin" of the person being treated. Furthermore, it would be necessary that the cells be injected into the patient when they are in the embryonic or fetal stage of development.

Cellular replacement will be made possible through cloning—a foreseeable advance in biotechnology by which random cells taken from the body could be stimulated into developing into a complete animal. Except for the red blood cells, each cell of the body contains an identical set of chromosomes, containing a genetic "blueprint" with the latent capability of becoming another complete organism—an identical twin of the person from whom the cell might be taken. A cell can be removed from any part of certain plants, put into an appropriate medium, and

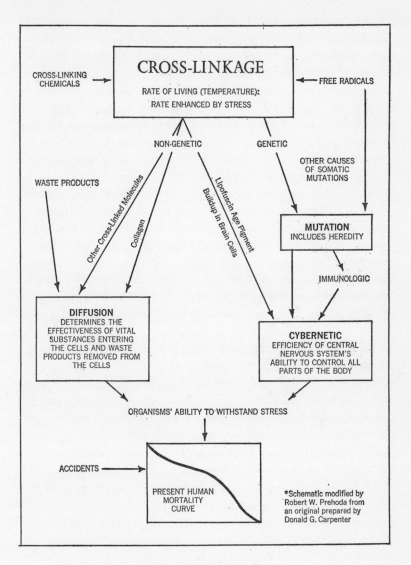

Figure 1: INTEGRATED THEORY OF AGING*

turned into an egg cell which thereafter develops into a complete plant. The same thing has been done with frogs.

As presently visualized, an ovum would be taken from a woman, and the nucleus (containing the genetic DNA) would be removed and replaced with a nucleus taken from a body cell of the person to be given the cellular replacement treatments. The altered ovum would then be stimulated into dividing and evolving into an embryo, which could be raised in a "host" mother, or in the more distant future, sustained through ectogenesis—the technique of test tube birth forecast by Aldous Huxley in his prophetic novel of the future, *Brave New World.*

The cellular replacement "identical twins" would be allowed to grow to a certain stage of embryonic or fetal development and then removed from the host mother or the ectogenesis chamber. The organs would be dissected and chemicals would cause the embryonic or fetal cells to separate. Then they could be injected into the patient's body, where liver cells would migrate to the liver, brain neurons would migrate to the brain, etc.

Now we come to the most difficult requirements of cellular replacement—making room for the new cells in the aging organs. Dying cells in the body are replaced by fibrous connective tissue largely composed of cross-linked collagen. This increasing mass of inert tissue would prevent the dissociated embryonic cells from effectively joining the vital portions of important body organs. The only solution to the connective tissue barrier is to break up cross-linked protein—particularly collagen. A youthful connective tissue should allow the replacement cells to fill in the gaps left by dying cells.

Though there are substances which will prevent cross-linking in newly-formed collagen, we have nothing that will break up old, heavily cross-linked collagen. *It is doubtful that cellular replacement can be successful without first perfecting means of ridding the body of cross-linked protein—particularly collagen.* Dr. Bjorksten's cross-linking theory and proposed therapy utilizing soil bacteria enzymes may be the key to slowing down the aging process and also provide the essential requirement for rejuvenation through cellular replacement.

Cellular replacement could assume a particularly important role in anti-aging therapy if somatic mutations cannot be prevented or controlled. It is conceivable that all of the permanent cells of vital organs, including the brain, may be slowly replaced over a period of many years.

Other anti-aging therapies are being refined. In 1923, the late Alexis Carrel proposed that our blood accumulates toxins which contribute to aging. New York's Dr. Norman Orentreich is experimenting with *plasmapheresis,* a technique in which blood is withdrawn and the red blood cells are separated from the plasma which is discarded. The blood cells are then mixed with a synthetic plasma and returned to the animal or human from which they were taken. It is assumed that the body will produce new blood protein molecules that will not cause the damage of those removed through plasmapheresis. Dr. Orentreich's research with dogs is encouraging, and plasmapheresis could become a widespread anti-aging therapy in the near future.

Treatments to slow and possibly reverse aging will become available within the next ten to fifteen years. Collectively, they will forever change society and the pattern of human life.

Demographic Problems are invariably raised when one proposes research that will extend the life-span of man. The world's present population of three and one-half billion is expected to rise to between six and seven billion by the year 2000. Some misguided persons have even proposed a moratorium on life-extending research—a stand analogous to solving unemployment by machine-gunning those so unfortunate as to be out of work. The simple facts of the matter are that advances in gerontology could not have any significant impact on population size during the next thirty years when the critical phase of the Malthusian dilemma is expected. Anti-aging treatments will be slowly adopted by the citizens of advanced countries, and they may be quite expensive at first. Only a small percentage effect can be expected by A.D. 2000, with no significant effect in the undeveloped areas.

The realization that the human life years will be significantly extended should contribute to the goal of world population stability. It will cause more people to realize that programs to restrict runaway population growth must be accelerated. If our descendants are to avoid an Orwellian "beehive" world, all forms of birth restriction—contraception, abortion, and sterilization—must be widely employed. A stable world population must be achieved even if the life-span does not change. Gerontology breakthroughs may be the key in stimulating public support for a massive worldwide birth restriction program.

Increased Economic Productivity will be one of the most significant benefits of gerontology. The pattern of our present medical research is to cure or delay specific diseases and prolong the period of senile decline. In contrast, controlling the aging process would extend youthful vitality and mental alertness. The world is becoming increasingly automated, so economic wealth is increasingly measured in scientific, artistic and scholarly productivity, which can be most easily increased by adding years and vitality to those who have already mastered their field.

Today, few professionals are really productive until they are thirty. The preceding years of education and apprentice status are a drain on society. With retirement at sixty-five, the ratio of years spent being educated to years productively working is about 1 to 1. The life-span of experimental rats has been doubled by gerontologists, and most of this increase was a period of youthful vigor. A 150-year life-span is, therefore, a reasonable expectation of gerontology. Doubling the life-span would allow the productive years to be extended to age 90 or even 120—education to productivity ratios of 1 to 2 and 1 to 3. Additional scientific gains could result in a 300-year life-span. Education to productivity ratios of 1 to 6 or 1 to 8 would then be feasible.

The painfully accumulated knowledge of a talented person is the greatest loss when it is removed by death or senility. There is probably very little true *wisdom* today, because many decades of experience are necessary for its formation. A wise population of supercentenarians could undertake projects undreamed of today. Multidisciplinary training with Ph.D. levels of education in several fields could become a feasible standard. Only youthful longevity will allow man to fully exploit the mental resources of the human brain.

Sociological Problems will be caused by longevity, but they have been exaggerated. Attitudes have been conditioned by the fact that conventional medical progress has greatly increased the number of senile persons with attendant problems of family adjustment, nursing home care, etc. As presently visualized, gerontological longevity gains will be years of added youth and not result in a percentage increase in our senile population. As more is learned about brain aging, senility may even be eliminated or significantly reduced.

The greatest sociological problems will center on the fact that people will continue working for a much longer period. The young have always been impatient for their superiors to step aside and allow them to assume positions of prestige and power. Advancements may come slowly, but there would be the satisfaction of knowing that the years spent "at the top" would be correspondingly longer. Quite possibly the "pyramid" structure that presently characterizes organizations will be replaced with an organizational framework of professional equals. Maybe the supercomputer will handle administration, and man could concentrate on innovation and synthesis. Vanity, greed, and variations in ambition may not allow this to be a complete solution, but there is such a trend in the "think factories" which are prototypes of tomorrow's organizations.

The greatest sociological problems would arise if longevity treatments are so expensive that they are not available to the entire population. Cellular replacement is likely to be costly. One could easily forecast a pattern in which an oligarchy of 300-year life-span geniuses—say 10 per cent of the population—ruled the masses who may only live an average of 120 years or so. This is very likely to be the pattern in undeveloped countries where already only a small elite have adequate medical services.

There has been much speculation that longevity would create a static and overly conservative society. People who are "old" by today's standards tend to reject change, but this could simply be the consequence of declining physical vigor and mental alertness. The elderly often have good memories of past events but tend to forget recent experiences because brain aging actually reduces learning ability. A double centenarian with the mental agility of youth would be innovative. Past societies with short average life-spans were static because of a lack of innovation, technological progress, and related education.

A two-hundred-year life-span might allow wealth and political power to become concentrated in the hands of a few men. Tax laws could reduce the concentration of wealth, but politicians are loath to limit their tenure. Longevity compounds the problems of a popular demagogue or a clever tyrant. The long-lived population would be better educated and "wiser." Hopefully, this would counteract adverse political patterns that may accompany extended life-span.

The advantages of the age of extended youth will far outweigh the adverse adjustments caused by longer life. For each reader there is a very personal question. *When?* Will the anti-aging therapies be refined soon enough for *you* to benefit? The probable key to success in controlling the aging process was invented by the Phoenicians: *money*—substantial financial support for gerontology. The answer to the question, therefore, depends on the level of funding that can be made available to fully exploring every promising approach to aging retardation.

The history of federal funding support for gerontology is a pattern that can only be described as *criminal* neglect. Less than $5 million a year is being spent on aging research by all government agencies combined. This is about one half of 1 per cent of our federal funds allotted to all biomedical R&D. To understand this shocking funding situation, one must have a brief outline of the biomedical research structure in Washington.

Government agencies can only support those biomedical research efforts that can be justified under the R&D "charter" of the agency. The Atomic Energy Commission's (AEC's) biomedical charter, for instance, is primarily concerned with the biological effects of radiation and means to protect humans from radiation damage. This somewhat limited charter has actually allowed quite a bit of AEC support for gerontology because radiation tends to accelerate the aging process. Grant requests can be written so that they fit into the restriction of the AEC research charter. The most important fact, however, is that AEC officials have been sympathetic to gerontology. They have helped scientists rewrite proposals so that they could be funded.

NASA and the military services have "mission oriented" biomedical research charters that only allow a disguised level of aging research to be supported. The charter of the National Science Foundation (NSF) is to support all basic research, and much of what we now know about the role of DNA and the genetic code in aging is due to NSF support. The NSF budget is restricted and must cover fundamental investigation in all the physical, biological, and social disciplines. Gerontology can only receive a small portion of the total.

The National Institutes of Health (NIH) is the government agency with the charter to support every branch of medical research including gerontology. NIH's total budget has exceeded $1 billion annually in recent years with about $800 million being awarded in research grants each year. Of this total, less than $1 million has been allotted each year to studies of biological aging, which is the most universal of all disease generators.

During all these years of gerontological research funding neglect, Dr. James A. Shannon (who retired in 1969) was the director of NIH. Most gerontologists contend that Dr. Shannon was not only reluctant to support gerontology, but was the source of administrative obstacles to a major program to control aging. In 1961, a White House Conference on Aging recommended the establishment of a separate Aging Institute within NIH to support a major program. Instead, gerontology was assigned as a "stepchild" to the National Institute of Child Health and Human Development where it is subsidiary to obstetrics, gynecology, and pediatrics. Aging grant requests are reviewed by scientists who have little or no knowledge of gerontology.

Dr. Shannon's attitude is characteristic of many unimaginative scientists who have always believed that aging was "part of nature's grand design" and not subject to modification. This conservative attitude has been the greatest obstacle that the gerontologists face. Several scientists have disguised their aging studies as cancer or heart investigations in order to receive NIH funding. It is not surprising that most of funds for aging have come from other government agencies and private sources.

All of the gerontologists mentioned in this chapter have experienced great difficulty obtaining research funds. Dr. Johan Bjorksten's experience typifies the deplorable pattern within NIH. In 1952, he formed a non-profit foundation in order to meet NIH requirements for research support. He received small aging grants from the Office of Naval Research, the Air Force, and the AEC. The J. M. Foundation donated $52,500, and Dr. Bjorksten spent over $60,000 of his own money on cross-linking research. His aging proposals have been strongly endorsed by several Nobel Laureates and many other leading scientists. Still no support from NIH!

I was told by the head of NASA's biomedical research program that he wanted to support cross-linking research, but it was simply not in his research charter. Similar statements were made by a number of scientific administrators in agencies outside of NIH. Some of Dr. Bjorksten's articles have been critical of NIH's neglect of aging research, and several knowledgeable observers have suggested that his candid but factual published views hindered his chances of receiving even token NIH funding.

After submitting proposals to NIH for fifteen years, Dr. Bjorksten decided to turn to American industry for the financial support needed to refine his enzyme therapy. In 1966, the

Upjohn Company of Kalamazoo, Michigan, entered into a sizable research program on cross-linkage with the Bjorksten Research Laboratories. The president of Upjohn indicated in one letter to me that the company was extremely pleased with the program's progress. Bjorksten's genius and persistence were able to keep his aging research program alive during the discouraging years of NIH neglect. Now the farsighted management of a major pharmaceutical company has undertaken a goal that should have been generously funded by NIH in the 1950s.

In 1968, the Association for the Advancement of Aging Research (AAAR) was formed by gerontologists in association with a number of leading citizens who are also concerned with the problem of funding neglect. Progress has been made under the dynamic leadership of its executive director, Dr. Bernard L. Strehler of the University of Southern California in Los Angeles. Largely through AAAR efforts, a bill is now before Congress to set up a commission to plan a comprehensive five-year "crash program" in gerontology. This program would be conducted by a new government agency. The AAAR is sponsoring symposia and attempting to refine a computerized aging R&D information storage and retrieval system that will be of great benefit to gerontologists.

In 1970, the American Aging Association (AGE) came into existence largely due to the tireless efforts of Dr. Denham Harman, whose antioxidant research is so promising. AGE is a society open to the general public and will raise research money in a manner similar to the American Heart Association and the National Cancer Society. AGE chapters are being established in every state, and annual fund-raising drives will allow readers to personally contribute to a program that will extend their own youth and total life-span. There is close coordination between AGE and AAAR, which is a more specialized professional organization. Together, they will hasten the day when the forecasts in this chapter become the reality of *your* life.

How long will man live in the age of extended youth? Many leading gerontologists contend that life-spans exceeding two or three hundred years may be feasible if the major causes of senescence can be corrected. Cellular replacement combined with truly massive breakthroughs in gerontology could bring about the one-thousand-year life-span forecast by Benjamin Franklin in 1780. The quest for long life, however, has caused some pseudoscientific proposals to be given considerable publicity. The most outlandish of these is the contention that people who presently die can be frozen and then revived in the future when they are to be restored to youth by the gerontologists of tomorrow's world.

Suspended animation may be achieved within the next twenty to thirty years, but not one leading scientist working in low-temperature biology believes that anyone frozen with today's primitive techniques could ever be revived. The tantalizing promise of an antediluvian life-span can only be realized by intense research in the years ahead. Low-temperature preservation of the elderly or those with a terminal disease may be an important part of future success when it comes, but again, generously funded research is a necessary first step.

The science of gerontology appears to be at about the same stage as was nuclear physics in the late 1930s when the discovery of uranium fission opened the door to atomic weapons and power plants. The 1970s and 1980s could be the decades when aging can be brought to a standstill. Such an achievement would be the most profound breakthrough in the history of science, for the conquest of aging is the conquest of time. It will give man the added years of youth to realize all of his rational dreams. We may soon be able to create a Methuselahian utopia which may include many readers whose life-spans will far exceed their current expectations.

2

R. C. W. ETTINGER

People Freezing:

The Establishment Thaws

The next author physicist Dr. R. C. W. Ettinger has described a means of achieving life beyond natural death. He advocates freezing bodies shortly after clinical death, preserving them in that state, and then, when science has progressed adequately, resuscitating them and curing their terminal disease. When his book, The Prospect of Immortality, *was published in 1964, cries of protest and objections were immediate and stringent. Damage to organisms in freezing and thawing is at present irreversible and the whole scheme seemed premature at best to many people and irresponsible and ludicrous to others.*

But immortality is a powerful incentive, and the alternatives to Ettinger's proposal risky. He has argued:

> *. . . To each his own, and to those who choose not to be frozen, all I can say is—rot in good health.*

Organizations and institutions have formed around the concept. Special cryogenic caskets are being manufactured; certain encouraging research has been performed; the attitudes of some early antagonists have softened. Most important of all, some people have already been frozen in the hope of being awakened later.

Dr. Ettinger brings us up to date in the following article.

In mid-1971, at least fourteen "dead" people have been frozen in hope of eventual rescue—i.e., restoration to active life, health, and even physical youth. The human cold storage concept first received wide attention in 1964, and the first human was frozen in 1966; now there exist physical facilities or/and organizations for this purpose in perhaps a score of states and foreign countries, and many leading experts in low-temperature biology have given at least tacit approval.

One might ask, how is it that so radical a notion, so outrageous a proposal, so shamelessly ambitious a project has had so much success so soon, so little active opposition? One might ask that, but of course I do not; I ask, instead, how it is that the greatest hope of all the ages has met so much passive resistance and so little enthusiasm, especially among scientists. The full answer to this question will require, and eventually receive, many-volumed excursions into psycho- and sociopathology; but a preliminary examination here may be useful, and will touch on several facets of the origin and development of *cryonics*.

EMANCIPATIONS, REVOLUTIONS, AND PERSPECTIVE

Cryogenics is an old word referring to low-temperature technology; *cryonics* is a recently coined word pertaining to human cold storage or "cryogenic interment." The purpose of cryogenic interment—as already intimated and more fully developed later —is nothing less than our emancipation from the ultimate bondage of death. (How ironic, that writers often refer to people being "freed" by death!—when in fact death is the complete, the absolute absence of freedom, since both power and will are reduced to nil.) The emancipation from death, seen as a historical process, in some ways resembles an earlier and lesser emancipation, that of the slaves in America.

Every great controversy sees people of intelligence and high principle on both sides, even though later ages may view one side as entirely in the right. For example, when the abolition of slavery was a political and social controversy, the abolitionists were considered radical; they were extremists. From our standpoint in history, we regard the abolitionists as having been entirely in the right, and those who wanted to preserve slavery as having been entirely in the wrong. But for a long time the weight of prestige and the influence of many great and good individuals was all on the side of preserving slavery.

Every revolution, every radically new program, encounters massive resistance at first, even if only the resistance of inertia and indifference. It is well known what Semmelweis went through with regard to the use of asepsis in surgery—how important that revolution was, how slow it was in making headway, and how great was the opposition of inertia.

Laymen almost always feel compelled to accept the consensus of "expert" opinion; but when there is a sharp break with tradition, and when the issue is laden with heavy emotional freight, the appeal to authority is virtually useless. The individual, whether scientist, physician, clergyman, or layman, has the onerous duty of evaluating the evidence, as best he can, and deciding for himself.

In the military field, by way of partial analogy, we do not blindly accept the advice of the experts on all occasions; in fact, the commander in chief of the U. S. Army (the President) and the second in command (the Secretary of Defense) are both civilians. They accept the responsibility of passing military judgment and sometimes overrule the experts. Despite their lack of training and detailed knowledge, through study and argument they acquire enough information about specific large issues to consider themselves—and to be—competent to pass judgment.

To gain perspective we must also remember that in emotional issues much seems to hinge on subtle nuances of psychology, on shades of meaning and turns of phrase. Those who bristle at the blasphemous notion of "resurrecting the dead" may be perfectly agreeable to "saving life." Those who are repelled by the thought of "another time around," or "imposing themselves on the future," may be attracted by the idea of new opportunities for adventure, growth and service. Only an imperceptible shift may be required to transform the pessimist, who sees the door of opportunity as nearly closed, into the optimist, who sees it beginning to open.

This shift is occurring. The climate of opinion, as I know from frequent public contacts, is steadily improving. But the change is still too slow; the same tired misconceptions and spurious objections are hanging on much too long, and repeated efforts are necessary to put the program and issues in focus.

As a prelude, for the benefit of the latecomers and the partially oriented, let us very briefly outline the history of cryonics.[1]

CRYONICS PRECURSORS

Faint and distorted intimations of our thesis have been around a very long time—perhaps almost as long as man himself. Certainly the ancient Egyptians attempted to preserve the bodies of the dead with the thought of resurrection, and the astonishing thing is that they may not have been far wrong. Mummies thousands of years old sometimes show much soft tissue partially preserved, including brains.[2] Recently, scientists have suggested that it may become possible to extract the genetic information from mummified animals, including humans, and grow organisms—"twins" of the deceased—from the cultured material. While this is very far from restoring the individual himself, still it would be most impressive.

About a century ago, C. A. Stephens tidied up the Egyptian notion and wrote, "Have your own body embalmed at your death in the hope that ere many decades death will be vanquished and the resurrection be brought within scientific possibilities."[3] Benjamin Franklin had similar ideas still earlier.[4] Stephens was overoptimistic as to the pace of progress, but the basic idea has not been proven wrong.

In the 1930s, Neil R. Jones wrote a science-fiction story about a Professor Jameson who arranged to have his body placed in an artificial satellite for perpetual frozen storage. (Jones apparently believed, mistakenly, that the "temperature of outer space," even at the earth's distance from the sun, is near absolute zero.) After millions of years, however, with humanity extinct, a wandering spaceship happens by, carrying aliens of such advanced accomplishments that they are able to revive his brain and endow it with indefinitely extended life, placing it in a mechanical body. Oddly enough, Jones never seemed to realize that what aliens might do, we might also, and that this offers hope for everyone.

Stories about "suspended animation" have been common, going back at least as far as Edmond About in nineteenth-century France.[5] These usually focused on freezing as the means of biostasis, but seldom linked suspended animation to extended life. They always seemed to assume freezing before clinical death, by non-lethal methods.

THE MODERN BEGINNING

In 1946, Jean Rostand first reported the protective effect of glycerine in freezing animal tissue, and this might be said to open the modern era of cryobiology (low-temperature biology) and put anabiosis on a footing of more than vague hope.[6] Rostand himself made part of our thesis explicit by predicting that one day the incurably ill would be frozen to await the time when technology would be equal to their requirements.[7]

Ideas about the relativity of death were also being deepened and broadened in the first half of this century, with thousands of people revived after clinical and legal death.[8] It was becoming clear that life is a set of complex processes and that death—the cessation of life—is not necessarily sudden, or complete, or irreversible. Rather, it is usually gradual, incomplete for a protracted period, and dependent for reversibility on the state of medical art; absolute criteria of reversibility, if they exist, are still unknown. These remarks apply, it is important to note, both to the organism and to its individual cells. In short, death may be regarded as a disease, not necessarily fatal.

Equally important, although less generally recognized, was the gradual emergence of the idea that deterioration with age may not be an inevitable consequence of living, as Bernard Strehler has noted.[9] Senile debility itself may be regarded as a disease, since it is a "deficiency relative to a desired norm," which is Joshua Lederberg's criterion.[10] This disease—the most insidious of all—may one day be preventable and even curable, allowing indefinitely extended life.

In 1947, I began to rediscover, integrate, clarify, extend, and develop these ideas. First publication was in a fiction story in 1948.[11] In 1960, I selected a couple of hundred names from Who's Who in America and tried to interest them by letter, but the very small and weak response made it clear that a convincing presentation would have to be of book length. The preliminary version of The Prospect of Immortality was privately published in 1962, and the expanded Doubleday edition in 1964.[12]

Despite the complex side issues in sociology, religion, economics, law, and philosophy, the basic proposition remains simple. The patient (we do not regard him as a cadaver and frown on Fred Pohl's "corpsesicle") should be frozen or otherwise preserved, as soon as possible after legal death, by the best available methods, even if these are "lethal" by present criteria. He will suffer, in general, six kinds of damage, due to (a) the fatal disease or injury; (b) the early stages of the dying process; (c) the crude freezing techniques; (d) old age (since most people die old); (e) the effects of long-term storage; and

(f) the effects of thawing. But deterioration in liquid nitrogen is thought to be negligible,[13] and no one will be thawed until these techniques are fully perfected, as proven by animal experimentation. Hence if it turns out that the first four kinds of damage are reversible—no matter how far in the future this is accomplished—the patient may one day be restored to active life and physical youth.

These ideas were beginning to stir in several minds in the early sixties, and probably occurred to many people independently. N. Duhring also published a book in 1962[14] and Lawrence N. Jensen was preparing to write one.[15]

RECENT EVENTS

It is not yet time, and this is not the place, to attempt a detailed tracing of the modern history of cryonics. (A partial history is available in Robert F. Nelson's book.[16]) Let us just note here a few highlights of recent years and the situation as of this writing.

At least fourteen people have been frozen, although only nine of those remain frozen; history, alas, has already seen its first mother-melter. Perhaps the best-known names are Professor James H. Bedford,[17] Marie Phelps Sweet,[18] and Steven Jay Mandell.[19] There have also been persistent rumors that certain wealthy and famous people have been quietly frozen, notably Walt Disney; but so far as I know, these are false.

Non-profit organizations active in the program have a probable membership of between one and two thousand. The Cryonics Society of New York[20] was formed in 1965 as a result of a schism, over activism, within the Life Extension Society.[21] There are now about a dozen Cryonics Societies in the United States, Europe, and South America; and in many locations there are "Cryonics Coordinators" who are laying the groundwork for additional Societies. At least four of the Societies—those of New York, California,[22] Michigan,[23] and France[24]—have physicians and morticians as members or/and in cooperation, and have substantial physical capabilities, including specially constructed equipment, e.g. mobile emergency units (special vans analogous to ambulances) and permanent storage units or cryonic suspension modules.

Led by Frederik Horn in New York and Joseph Klockgether in California, several morticians have given active cooperation; and the National Funeral Directors Association has moved, in the course of four years, from cautious hostility to cautious approval.[25] Colleges of mortuary science have repeatedly invited our speakers, as have medical colleges.

The first permanent storage units, or "cryocapsules," were made by Cryo-Care Equipment Co. of Phoenix, Arizona.[26] These could be described as giant dewars or thermos bottles, with an inner cylinder of aluminum (because ordinary steel becomes brittle at liquid nitrogen temperature), an outer cylinder of steel, and an evacuated space between for insulation, with multiple radiation barriers of aluminized mylar. These units, varying in design, are about ten feet long, four feet in diameter, and weigh one thousand pounds empty; a charge of liquid nitrogen lasts several months. They sold for roughly $4,000, and reportedly required about $300 annually for liquid nitrogen. Currently, storage units are being made by Minnesota Valley Engineering Co., one of the older and larger cryogenics firms.

Religious objection to cryonics has been minimal, with most major denominations apparently taking it in stride. There has been at least one formal Roman Catholic funeral after freezing, and at least one Orthodox Jewish; and many clergymen have written favorably.[27]

There has been at least one instance of formal legal recognition: Bronson La Follette, the attorney general of Wisconsin, has written that in his opinion cryonic suspension is lawful in that state.[28] A committee of attorneys of the Cryonics Society of New York has prepared suggested legal documents—to be modified for the individual and the jurisdiction—intended to give reasonable assurance that the patient's wishes will be carried out.[29]

The earliest permanent or semipermanent storage facilities were those of the Cryo-Care company in Phoenix, licensed by the city as a laboratory. Patients currently are being stored in California and New York. Cryonic Interment, Inc., has a facility in a cemetery near Los Angeles.[30] Cryo-Span Corp. is operating in New York, led by attorney Curtis Henderson and editor Saul Kent.[31] There is a physical facility called Hope Knoll, near Appleton, Wisconsin, built by engineer Joseph Cannon, but it has not yet cleared all legal hurdles. Other companies are in the organizational stage.[32]

ADVANCES IN RESEARCH

Meanwhile, cryobiological research has advanced somewhat in recent years, despite the scant support it receives and despite the almost total lack of full-time workers in this field. Gains are being made in the understanding of freezing damage.[33] Although supposedly knowledgeable people are repeatedly quoted in the press to the effect that we still cannot successfully freeze "even a single organ," there have been several successes or partial successes. Ralph Hamilton and Herndon Lehr have frozen a segment of a dog's small intestine for a week at liquid nitrogen temperature, with full restoration of function after thawing.[34] N. A. Halasz and colleagues have reported the long-term survival of dog kidneys after freezing to below $-50°$ C; and the kidney is a very complex organ with many functions. Even more spectacular, although less unequivocal, were the results of Professor Isamu Suda and colleagues at Kobe University; the brains of several cats were frozen, one for over six months, with a fairly good corticogram—brain wave tracing—after thawing.[35] The brain is of course by far the most important organ, being the principal seat of the personality and memory; in fact, many physicians advocate using brain waves as the main indication of life or death, so that one could make a case for saying that we have already achieved suspended animation!

There has recently been another striking vindication of cryonicist optimism, upsetting the notion, held by almost every physician, that a few minutes without blood causes "irreversible" brain damage. In 1970, it was proven by Dr. Peter Gouras in the United States and by Hossman and Sato in Germany that the mammalian brain can recover fully after at least an hour of total ischemia at normal body temperature! (See *Science*, April 17, 1970.)

THE SCIENTIST'S DOUBLE STANDARD AND PROBABILITY THEORY

How is it possible that so many men of intelligence, good will, and expert knowledge are still cool to cryonics? The answer is multifold, since the scientist has many facets to his personality and cryonics touches on every nerve and gland; the root cause, in most cases, lies in neurosis, in irrational pathways of fear. But right now I want to look at the shortcomings of these scientists qua scientists.

The ugly central fact is that most of them have simply been irresponsible, making offhand statements about our program that they would never dream of making in a technical journal.

There have been many public statements to the effect that if someone is frozen by present methods the chance of revival—ever—is "negligible" or "remote" or "vanishingly small." Well, if someone says the chance is "negligible," that merely means that *he* is willing to neglect it. But if someone says the chance is "vanishingly small," he is simply lying. The proof is easy: Ask him the simplest and most obvious questions. "How do you know? What is your proof? Where are your calculations?" These "experts" have no answers to such questions; they can only point out, lamely, that the repair job will be exceedingly difficult—*measured against their estimate of future capability*. But our knowledge of the nature and extent of freezing and thawing damage is limited, and anyone who thinks he can estimate the limits of scientific capability in the indefinite future is irresponsible. No one, to my knowledge, has even *pretended* to make such an estimate on any rational basis, let alone succeeded. This is hard for a layman to appreciate, but should be easy for a scientist.

Perhaps some of these men suffer more from ignorance than irresponsibility; maybe they know a lot about biology, but little about probability theory. Yet a little reflection should convince them that the probability of revival is not small; it is simply unknown, which is not at all the same thing. The point is so important that it may be justified to belabor it a bit; we can illuminate it by a partial analogy with the "evidence" for extrasensory perception.

Dr. Joseph B. Rhine and others have used statistics in an attempt to prove that mental telepathy and similar phenomena exist; Dr. Rhine's "evidence" consisted mainly in anomalously high scores on card-guessing tests.[36] He could never understand the fundamental absurdity of his premise, viz., that "extra chance" was synonymous with "ESP." In actuality, to prove ESP, he had to compare the probability of ESP with the probability of other non-chance explanations (cheating, etc.); unless this could be done, quantitatively his results not only meant little, they meant *nothing*. Somewhat similarly, no degree of difficulty of repair, however appalling to present-day science, means *anything whatever* unless quantitatively measured against rationally computed probable future capability of repair.

It is possible, in principle, to estimate or make a calculation of probability for any event, past or future, repetitive or not. Yet in many cases experimental uncertainties or imponderables of the future make calculation virtually useless. This is our situation with respect to the event "future technology will allow repair of injury inflicted by present freezing methods." We want to minimize risks and maximize chances by every means, but we cannot actually assign a number to the probability of success with even moderate confidence.

JUDGING A GAMBLE

The reluctant scientist can, and often does, take final refuge in his "feelings"; he cannot prove the chance is small, but nevertheless feels it is. The giveaway is his frequent use of the word "negligible," which merely may mean, as already pointed out, that he is a pessimist. There are two sore points here, both related to value judgments.

First, it is clearly not cricket for the scientist, if he happens to value extended life lightly, to use his prestige *as a scientist* to browbeat laymen. Personal values must be kept distinct from scientific judgments. This is *especially* true when his professional competence is in question—and no one is competent to make confident predictions about the distant future. The appeal to authority is almost completely spurious.

Second, the deprecator can easily obscure another vital point: The worth of a gamble depends not only on the chance of success, but also on the value of success; in fact, the "expected gain" is just the product of these two numbers, the probability of success and the payoff. Even if the chance of repair was minuscule—which I do not concede—the prize is so enormous, in the view of some people, that the effort would still be justified. Although there is not—I emphasize, not—a very close parallel, we can make a partial comparison with the Irish Sweepstakes.

The probability of success in the Sweepstakes is very small; yet the prize, for many, is attainable in no other way. Unless they buy tickets, they will *surely* die poor, whereas the chance of winning brightens drab lives. Hence it is not necessarily wrong to participate, even though the expected gain is negative in this case—the probability of success, multiplied by the prize, is less than the cost of a ticket. In the cryonics sweepstakes, this is emphatically not true; the expected gain may be tremendous, both in dollars and in the intangibles. An interesting sidelight is that the Irish Sweepstakes generate money for hospitals, and we do have a good parallel here: The cryonics program is generating money for research in cryobiology and gerontology, with potential benefit to everyone, regardless of the fate of individuals.

THE ARROGANCE OF PESSIMISM

So very many scientists are so very confident that this or that will "never" be accomplished! And they are so unaware that they are revealing childish egotism! They are saying, in effect: "I cannot imagine how this thing could be accomplished; therefore nobody, even from the vantage point of a later era, will ever be able to do so." What sublime conceit!

We need not agree that "anything is possible." In fact, the number of things that are not possible must be enormously greater than things that are possible. Just the same, every generation of scientists is surprised to find that the end has not yet arrived. Regardless of lip service to radical change, every generation, with the exception of a few hardy souls, seems to think that all the revolutions are past and that only minor refinements are left.

We need not dwell on the ludicrous failures of nerve and imagination so frequent among some distinguished scientists in the past, including the recent past. But it might be salutary to point out that some would-be prophets can suffer not only from myopia and astigmatism, so to speak, but also from hypermetropia. Even so great a speculator as Herbert George Wells sometimes exhibited this farsightedness, which obscured his nearer vision.

Wells could see and convey to others the mighty sweep of history, the bizarre possibilities of the dim future, and the grandeur of man's destiny. Yet when he turned from the distant to the near future, when he tried to change himself from the philosopher-poet to engineer, he became commonplace and made commonplace mistakes.

Some of his minor visions were reasonably accurate: He predicted, occasionally with some detail, such things as automatic dishwashers and electric ranges.[37] But he also sometimes fell on his face with a painful thud:

"I must confess that my imagination, in spite even of spurring, refuses to see any sort of submarine doing anything but suffocating its crew and foundering at sea . . . a first-rate man who has been breathing carbonic acid and oil vapor under a pressure of four atmospheres becomes presently a second-rate man."[38] This was in 1914.

Clearly, as Wells tried to grapple with the details of a problem, he lost the Big Picture. When Wells the amateur engineer was allowed to face Wells the visionary, the latter was overcome with confusion. For just this reason the cryobiologists, for example, are nearly the worst possible people to ask about the chance of reviving those frozen by crude methods: They are so familiar with the difficulties, and so impressed by them, and so devoid of any present ability to cope with them, that they tend to pessimism. And although there is a pleasant legend that great men tend to be humble, my experience suggests the contrary: The more exalted the expert, the more rigid he is likely to be in his insistence that what he cannot conceive now, no one can accomplish ever.

TWO EXTREME VIEWS

Until very recently, in fact, the experts clustered near the extreme lower boundary of pessimism or conservatism, which is the recommendation that no one should be frozen until success is assured. Idiotic as it sounds, this view is actually expressed by many scientists and physicians. It means, presumably, that we must wait until someone has been frozen, stored, revived, rejuvenated, and has lived forever. More seriously, it means that we cannot place any reliance *whatever* on future advances in repair; we must assume that damage not reparable now will never be reparable. (And we must lump in thawing damage with freezing damage.) Such an attitude cannot be explained in terms of logic or science, but only sociology or psychiatry.

The view at the opposite extreme—in which I concur—was expressed by Professor Gerald Feinberg of Columbia University: "I believe . . . a good first approximation for . . . predictions is to assume that everything will be accomplished that does not violate known fundamental laws of science, as well as many things that do violate these laws."[39] In other words, if something is possible in principle, then if we want it enough it will be accomplished in practice, sooner or later, regardless of how formidable the difficulties appear; and even if it is now thought to be actually impossible in principle, it may nevertheless turn out to be feasible.

Through no coincidence, Dr. Feinberg is a member of the Cryonics Society of New York. He is also the author of a paper in the *Physical Review*—the world's leading journal of research in physics—which stunned the scientific world and may revolutionize both science and industry.[40] In this paper he showed that, contrary to the previous opinion of almost every scientist, including Einstein himself, the theory of special relativity does not necessarily preclude the existence of particles traveling faster than light *in vacuo*. His hypothetical "tachyons" have also been discussed in many lay periodicals.[41]

If the existence of tachyons is verified—and university laboratories in the United States and Europe are spending substantial sums of money looking for them—there will be staggering theoretical and practical consequences; it will amount to a fourth major advance in physics, comparable to those of the Newtonian era, relativity, and quantum theory, and Professor Feinberg will take his place among the giants of history. But even if tachyons do not exist, the electrifying shock to scientists is scarcely diminished. It has been shown, once more, that things may be achieved that were thought to be not only improbable but downright impossible. This new lesson in humility is sorely needed.

CRYONICS AND MEDICAL ETHICS

Like the scientists, most physicians remain pessimistic and noncommittal. Let us consider the ethics of their position.

Tending, apparently, to justify reluctance is the tradition that rejects the use of any but proven methods on human patients; and this principle fits well with the natural inclination not to exert oneself or expose oneself to criticism. This combination, in fact, dominates the current thinking of most physicians (with some notable exceptions). In addition, there is a school of medical thought that recommends, in principle, against the use of extraordinary efforts to save "useless" patients. (There was a well-publicized scandal in England a few years back about the notation "NTBR" on the beds of elderly patients—"Not to be resuscitated" in event of heart failure.)

Yet the vital core of the medical ethic is that the patient comes first—not society, not the family, and certainly not the physician's convenience, but the patient—and that even heroic measures are justified in the attempt to prolong life, especially if the patient requests it. Furthermore, there is wide recognition that desperate cases justify desperate measures: Unproven remedies are permissible if the patient has no other hope.

The latter viewpoint was publicized widely in the fall of 1967, when Dr. Christiaan Barnard appeared on American television after the first heart transplant. He had been criticized for using an insufficiently tested technique, but calmly pointed out that the patient had no other chance. If this reasoning is valid, as most seem to agree, then it applies even more forcefully to cryonics. After all, Dr. Barnard actually killed his patient, in a sense, since he cut his heart out, and the net result might have been to shorten his life, whereas the cryonics patients are already clinically dead and have nothing at all to lose.

Another point with a close parallel in cryonics was made on the same TV program by an American participant, the celebrated surgeon Dr. C. W. Lillehei. Dr. Lillehei pointed out that Dr. Barnard's operation gave hope to countless other heart patients, and therefore constituted a therapeutic achievement in itself, regardless of the outcome. Just so, and more so, with cryonic suspension! The patient "dies" with an extra measure of hope, and the family's grief is mitigated; these are substantial benefits, whatever the medical sequel. This is not guesswork; we have firsthand reports—the patients and their families were comforted. Typically, Mrs. Pauline Mandell, mother of twenty-four-year-old Steven Mandell, who was frozen by the Cryonics Society of New York in July of 1968, said: ". . . there is so much less feeling of loss when there is a flicker of hope . . . there is a light at the end of the tunnel."[42]

Needless to say, the feeling of hope does not by itself justify unusual medical measures; if it did, every con artist and fakir could make a good case for himself. (And some would say that certain of the world's religions represent a similar kind of swindle and delusion.) But when it can be shown that the hope is rational, and when there are additional benefits such as impetus and support for research, then we are on solid ground.

Understanding is slowly increasing, and medical participation in our program is also. The early fears of scandals and ostracism have proven empty; there has been no hysteria, and the medical and other professionals who have assisted in cryonic suspension have not suffered. The first chairman of the Bay Area Cryonics Society (San Francisco) was Dr. M. Coleman Harris, a highly respected physician who has earned many medical honors; and many other physicians are members of the Cryonics Societies or are cooperating with them. But neither the growth of awareness nor the degree of awareness are adequate to the challenge, so far. The minimum moral requirement has been expressed by theologian Robert Johansen, Crozer Theological Seminary:

"Doctors and ministers who, by not at least *explaining* the freezer program, are actually making a decision about the lives of their followers without even consulting them. Whether or not one favors cryonic suspension, it is my belief that it should at least be made known as an option. That is to say, even a chance of success offers enough merit for close examination by all those who are honestly concerned about life."[43]

By acquainting his patients with the opportunity, the physician is not getting himself out on any limb. After all, there is no problem of availability of a new drug or learning of an esoteric technique or of legal permission. The physician does not have to perform any physical services, if he prefers not to. Cryonics Society personnel will take over, if appropriate arrangements can be made in time. The minimum we ask—and the minimum the patient has a right to expect—is that the opportunity be made known, in time. In this case, silence is not golden, but perhaps the blood red of negligent homicide.

RESEARCH AND CRYONICS

There is one more foible of many scientists and physicians, important enough for separate attention: the notion that "we should spend our money on research, not on cryonic suspension." This is nonsense on its face and on the record.

To begin with, as repeatedly emphasized, those dying now cannot wait for more research, but must be given the benefit of whatever chance current methods offer. Most of us, if we are in our right minds, have limited interest in abstract humanity or remote posterity; we are primarily concerned with those near us and cannot forego their probable physical benefit and certain psychological benefit. But even on their own terms, those who complain that "research should come first" are wrong.

Cryonics does not divert money from research, but channels money into research, and it is the *only* likely source of such funds in large amounts. Those who speak of using the funds for research "instead" of cryonics are out of touch with reality: These are not the alternatives. This is scarcely even arguable; it is a matter of record.

Cryobiology has always been ill supported, and in recent years support seems actually to have dwindled, partly because of a cutback in NASA funds. And private efforts to raise research funds have had very little success—as witness, for example, the Society for Anabiosis.[44]

In contrast, organizations growing directly out of the cryonics program have donated money to cryobiological research without the help of a single big name: these include the Cryonics Societies of America, the Harlan Lane Foundation, and the Bedford Foundation. The sums involved have so far been very modest, but they are growing. Note, for example, that Professor James Bedford, not a very wealthy man, left a substantial portion of his estate—$100,000 of it—for research in cryobiology and related areas which he certainly would not have done had he not arranged cryonic suspension for himself.[45] Does it require much imagination to see how this research will fare when people are being frozen by the thousands, or by the millions?

The can-rattling approach to fund-raising and appeals to a vague and diffuse altruism or abstract principle are unlikely to produce more than small change. But a dynamic cryonics program will mean personal involvement and emotional commitment, and the will to apply *major* resources to research. Note carefully, once more, that this is not conjecture: It is happening. I personally know many individuals in our Societies who are devoting major energies to the program and making many sacrifices to assure their families' preparations.

We in the Cryonics Societies intend to extend and systematize our efforts to support research in cryobiology, gerontology, and related disciplines. The measures contemplated include a routine percentage allocation of all funds and organized solicitation of foundations and individuals, as well as lobbying. (The latter activities will be important only in the short run; the program itself, once it reaches critical mass, will generate all the money the biologists can possibly absorb.) Needless to say, our success will depend substantially on the support we receive from the scientific community. A positive feedback is involved: Cryonics and cryobiology need each other, and to speak of either as coming "first" is nearly meaningless.

THE SCIENTIFIC ADVISORY COUNCIL

In 1968, a breakthrough was achieved in relations with the scientific community. Until then, very few scientists, especially in biological and medical disciplines, had been willng to associate themselves with us publicly, although many had given informal expressions of sympathy. But by the middle of 1968, through a protracted communications effort, I estimate that a full half of American cryobiologists had come around to a position at least of tolerance or passive approval. In forming the Scientific Advisory Council of the Cryonics Societies of America, we did not insist that the members fully endorse all of our positions and programs, but that, in addition to assisting us in areas of common concern, they give formal recognition to the principle of free individual choice and to the fact that the probability of revival is not small but only unknown. This was done, and the Council now includes important names in cryobiological research, as well as in other areas of science and medicine.[46] While the effect will be gradual, we expect that the existence of the Council and its activities will greatly strengthen cryonics, both in technology and in public relations.

WHERE THE BUCK STOPS

The sense of the foregoing discussion, as the reader will perceive, is that cryonics is a going concern, that success is nearly inevitable, and that its development is only a matter of time. But there's the rub: Some of us don't have much time, and almost all of us have less than we think. This is why we find so infuriating the attitude of the typical citizen, who smiles in vague benediction, nods agreeably that science is wonderful, and mumbles something about making arrangements for himself and his family "when the process is perfected." He is so stupefied by the institutionalization of everything that he has no sense of personal responsibility; and he has no understanding of "lead time."

The latter concept is very easy to grasp, intellectually, but extremely difficult on an emotional level, somewhat as the danger of running into the street is easy for children to talk about, but requires long training for them to *appreciate*. The cryonics program must be supported *now*, if it is to be scientifically and administratively advanced enough to maximize the chances of those dying *later*. We need fully perfected freezing methods, and we need a vast network of hair-trigger emergency centers. (Eventually, it may be routine to wear an electronic pulse-watcher which will flash a coded distress signal whenever the heart falters, a little like the devices now used in the intensive-care wards of hospitals.) The methods and the network cannot bloom overnight; they must grow, bit by bit, and a later or slower start necessarily means a later maturity.

Those parents who imagine their children to be in no early danger, and think therefore that cryonics has no urgency for them, are taking false comfort. Not only can death come without warning, but their chances fifty years hence may depend on actions taken now. We do not delude ourselves that the perfection of freezing methods will necessarily be easy; it is conceivable that, even with massive support, it will take another generation, although we hope not. If those dying now are to have any chance, and those dying later a maximum chance, the cryonics program must be implemented on a large scale—now!

Let us not deceive ourselves, either, that we can implement cryonic suspension on a selective basis—freeze only those who die under "good" conditions. We do not know where to draw the line, and a line-drawing attitude would effectively amount to paralysis. There must be no excuses and no exceptions. It must become habitual to freeze the "deceased," regardless of how unfavorable the circumstances may appear. Only thus can morale be maintained, and only thus can we make rapid progress.

After all, we are at war. The ancient enemy will take ruthless advantage of every weakness, every hesitation. He will give no quarter and allow no second chances. We must not abandon our fallen, however grievous their wounds. Each time we do our duty, we strengthen the program and gain confidence that those on whom we rely will, in turn, do their duty by us.

Governments and institutions protect our interests with reasonable efficiency much of the time, and we tend to rely on them. But by their nature they are sluggish, slow to react to new dangers or new opportunities. Just as the frontiersman of the old West knew that only his own vigilance, courage, strength, and skill stood between his family and mortal danger, so must we recognize our individual responsibility on the cryonics frontier.

When Harry Truman was President of the United States, he kept a reminder mounted on his office wall: THE BUCK STOPS HERE. I suggest that each of us look at the faces in his family and ask himself, where does the buck stop?

REFERENCES

1. The term "cryonics," referring to the activities surrounding human cold storage, was coined by Karl Werner, then vice-president of the Cryonics Society of New York.

2. Don Brothwell and Eric Haggs, editors, *Science in Archeology*, Thames & Hudson, Bristol, 1963.

3. Gerald J. Gruman, "A History of Ideas About the Prolongation of Life," Transaction of the American Philosophical Society, 56:9, 1966.

4. Ibid.

5. Edmond About, *The Man with the Broken Ear.*

6. Jean Rostand, "Glycerine et Resistance du Sperme aux Basses Temp.," *C. R.* Acad. Sci., Paris V. 222:1542, 1946.

7. "Revivre Apres La Mort," *Science et Vie*, May 1963.

8. "The Reversal of Death," *Saturday Review*, Aug. 4, 1962.

9. B. L. Strehler, *Time, Cells, and Aging*, Academic Press, 1962.

10. He said it, but I can't find the reference.

11. R. C. W. Ettinger, "The Penultimate Trump," *Startling Stories,* March 1948.

12. R. C. W. Ettinger, *The Prospect of Immortality,* privately published, 1962; Doubleday & Company, 1964; Macfadden-Bartell, 1966; Denoel, Paris, 1964 (as *L'Homme est-il Immortel?*); Agon, Amsterdam, 1964 (as *De diepvriesmens*); Sidgwick & Jackson, London, 1965; Hyperion, Freiburg, 1965 (*Aussicht auf Unsterblichkeit?*); Rizzoli, Milan, 1967 (*Ibernazione Nuova Era*).

13. H. T. Meryman, "Mechanics of Freezing in Living Cells and Tissues," *Science,* Vol. 124, 1956.

14. N. Duhring, *Immortality: Physically, Scientifically, Now,* privately published, 1962.

15. Professor and chairman, Art Department, Castleton State College, Castleton, Vermont.

16. R. F. Nelson and Sandra Stanley, *We Froze the First Man,* Dell, 1968.

17. See e.g., the Los Angeles *Herald Examiner,* Jan. 14, 1967, p. 1.

18. See e.g., the Glendale (Calif.) *News-Press,* Sept. 2, 1967.

19. See e.g., *Newsweek,* Aug. 12, 1968, p. 29.

20. 9 Holmes Court, Sayville, Long Island, N.Y. 11782.

21. 2011 N St. N.W., Washington, D.C. 20036.

22. 216 Pico Blvd., Suite 3, Santa Monica, Calif. 90405.

23. 24041 Stratford, Oak Park, Mich. 48237.

24. Société Cryonics de France, 10, rue Thiboumery, Paris 15, France; Anatole Dolinoff, president.

25. See e.g., "How Embalmers Can Serve the Living," by Murray Shor, *Casket and Sunnyside,* June 1968.

26. 2204 W. Indian School Rd., Phoenix, Ariz.; E. F. Hope, president.

27. See e.g., John Warwick Montgomery, "Cryonics and Orthodoxy," *Christianity Today,* May 10, 1968, Vol. XII, No. 16.

28. Written opinion of the attorney general to the State Health Officer, Nov. 1, 1967.

29. Available through the Cryonics Societies. Chairman of the committee was Professor David Haber, Rutgers University Law School.

30. For information, write the Cryonics Society of California, address above (22).

31. For information, write the Cryonics Society of New York, address above (20).

32. For information about Continuelife Corporation, write Forrest Walters, 131 Avenue C., Latrobe, Pa. 15650.

33. See e.g., A. M. Karow, Jr., and W. R. Webb, "Tissue Freezing: A Theory for Injury and Survival," *Cryobiology,* 2:3:99, 1965.

34. R. W. Hamilton and H. B. Lehr, "Survival of Small Intestine after Storage for 7 Days at $-196°$ C," *Cryobiology,* 3:375, 1967.

35. I. Suda, K. Kito, and C. Adachi, "Viability of Long Term Frozen Cat Brain *in vitro,*" *Nature,* Vol. 212, Oct. 15, 1966.

36. J. B. Rhine, *The Reach of the Mind*, William Sloane Associates, Inc., New York, 1947. Also various issues of the *Journal of Parapsychology*.

37. H. G. Wells, *Anticipations of the Action of Mechanical and Scientific Progress upon Human Life and Thought*, Chapman & Hall Ltd., London, 1914.

38. Ibid.

39. Gerald Feinberg, "Physics and Life Prolongation," *Physics Today*, Nov. 1966.

40. Gerald Feinberg, "Possibility of Faster-Than-Light Particles," the *Physical Review*, July 25, 1967.

41. See e.g., *Time*, Feb. 14, 1969.

42. Newark *Star-Ledger*, Aug. 1, 1968; also see e.g., *Newsweek*, Aug. 12, 1968.

43. Robert Johansen, "Cryonics and the Cross: Reflections on Immortality," Proceedings of the Second Annual National Cryonics Conference, in press.

44. Now defunct.

45. Los Angeles County Probate File No. 518938, filed Feb. 14, 1967, book 1819, p. 144.

46. For a current listing of the Scientific Advisory Council, write one of the Cryonics Societies. Besides those listed above (20, 22, 23, 24) there are now: Bay Area Cryonics Society, 1460 Mills Court, Menlo Park, Calif. 94025; Cryonics Society of Kentucky, 326 E. College St., Louisville, Ky.; Northeast Cryonics Society, c/o Dr. R. D. Enzmann, 29 Adams St., Lexington, Mass.; Northwest Cryonics Society, Route 4, Box 240, Gresham, Oreg. 97030; Cryonics Society of Pennsylvania, 131 Avenue C, Latrobe, Pa. 15650; Cryonics Society of Brazil, c/o Prof. J. A. Castro, Roue Alvaro Alvina, 21, 8 Andar, Rio de Janeiro; Sociedad Cryonics de Colombia, c/o Ricardo Vejarano Varona, Carrera 5a, No. 16–14, Oficina 301, Bogota; Deutscher Cryonics Club, c/o Rudolf Burkhart, 8000 Munchen 13, Hohenzollernstrasse 110, West Germany.

3

G. FEINBERG

What Are Tachyons, and What Could We Do with Them?

Contrary to popular belief, Einstein's theory of relativity does not exclude the possibility of faster-than-light particles, it only excludes the possibility of particles moving at that speed. Some physicists have argued recently that if matter were somehow already moving faster than the speed of light it could exist without violating our concepts of nature. Dr. Gerald Feinberg, a young professor of physics at Columbia University, has been concerned with the quantum aspects of the problem; he coined the term "tachyon" for these hypothetical particles. In the following article, Dr. Feinberg describes some of the strange properties tachyons would have, and should they be discovered, some uses which man of the future might choose to make of them. Dr. Feinberg recently wrote The Prometheus Project, *a book describing the need for and characteristics of important world goals which in their pursuit would unify men and nations of the world. Perhaps the search for the tachyon is one such goal.*

It has been generally believed by scientists that according to Einstein's theory of relativity, the greatest speed at which energy can be transmitted from point to point in space is the speed of light in vacuum, or approximately 300,000 kilometers per second. In the last few years, however, several physicists have proposed that this conclusion should be modified.[1] They agree that the theory of relativity does imply that the objects composing ordinary matter and all the other known elementary particles indeed cannot travel faster than light. However, they point out that relativity does allow for the existence of other objects, yet undiscovered, which have the contrary property of always traveling faster than light. These hypothetical objects have been called tachyons, from the Greek word meaning swift. For tachyons the speed of light is also a limiting speed, but it is a lower limit rather than an upper limit. The speed of a tachyon can take on any value between 300,000 km./sec. and infinity.

Because tachyons obey the theory of relativity as do other objects, many of their properties can be directly determined from that theory. In particular, the relations between energy, speed, and momentum for tachyons are given by:

$$E = \frac{\mu c^2}{\sqrt{v^2/c^2 - 1}} , \tag{1}$$

$$p = \frac{\mu v}{\sqrt{v^2/c^2 - 1}} . \tag{2}$$

Here E is the energy, p the momentum, and v the speed of a tachyon. c is the speed of light, and μ is a positive number characteristic of the tachyon. It may be seen from these equations that E and p are real quantities, as they must be, provided that v/c is greater that 1, i.e., as long as the tachyon travels faster than light.

It follows from these equations that the energy and momentum of a tachyon decrease as its speed increases. In the limiting case as the speed approaches infinity, the energy approaches zero, while the momentum decreases to the finite value $p = \mu c$. This last property is of some importance for one of the possible applications of tachyons as an exhaust for interstellar rockets, as will be seen below.

Experimental searches for tachyons until now have given negative results.[2] However, these experiments may not have completely excluded their existence. Let us therefore consider what uses might be made of tachyons if we should discover them. Of necessity, we must discuss what is theoretically possible, rather than engineering details, which can hardly be worked out before tachyons are actually found and studied further.

The most obvious uses of tachyons would come in connection with interstellar travel. It is well known that a mismatch exists between the present human life-span, the distances to other stellar systems, and the maximum speed at which we could hope to travel in the absence of tachyons. Several pessimistic studies of interstellar travel have been written on this basis, which have concluded that such travel was forever impossible for us.[3] We shall see that these conclusions are not necessarily justified if we can indeed discover and control tachyons.

Let us first note that there is no question of human beings physically traveling faster than light. We are made of ordinary (non-tachyonic) matter, and as such come under the relativistic injunction forbidding such matter to exceed light speed. It might however be thought that we could at least use tachyon beams to communicate rapidly between the stars. It could even be imagined that some form of information transfer might be developed in which the total information content of the atoms of a person could be transmitted by tachyons at speeds greater than light, and the information used to reconstruct the person at some other place, thus providing a form of rapid transit. After all, atoms are the same everywhere in the universe, and it is the pattern according to which these atoms are distributed that determines whether they are a man or a mass of carbon, oxygen, etc.

However, there is reason to believe that tachyons, even if they exist, will not be usable for any form of communication. This is because one property that tachyons must have implies a very high and uncontrollable noise to signal ratio in any channel using them. To see this, we note that a device which emits tachyons, as viewed by one observer, will instead absorb tachyons when viewed by some other observers who are in motion relative to the first observer. But whereas an emitter of tachyons does not imply the existence of any detector for the tachyons emitted, in order to absorb tachyons, it is necessary that there be a source of them somewhere. If for one observer, a tachyon is emitted without being detected, i.e., escapes to outer space, then for the other observer, tachyons must come from outer space to be absorbed.

Now suppose that we try to build a communicator using tachyons. Then we must have a device that emits tachyons, in some regular form, that can be received elsewhere and interpreted. Any message sent in this way will be viewed by some other observer as originating elsewhere and coming to our emitting device to be absorbed. But viewed in this way, the message cannot depend on whether our device is present or not, since the content of a message coming from elsewhere cannot depend on whether there happens to be a receiver present to detect it. Hence we can only send those messages which would be in transit whether or not our emitter exists. But this is as good as saying that we cannot transmit messages at all, since the eventual receiver could never know whether the tachyon he received was sent purposefully, or whether it was one of the large number of tachyons that are traveling through space independently of any emitter.

It is conceivable that the situation will turn out to be more favorable than this. There may be certain regions of the tachyon spectrum which, for a particular observer represents a "clear channel," in that the tachyon background is weak or absent. Under these circumstances tachyonic messages might be transmitted in this channel. But we will not know if this situation exists until we are able to detect tachyons, and explore the flux of them in the environment, in various energy regions.

What use could tachyons then be to us if we do discover them, leaving aside their unlikely use in communications? I believe that their most important application might well be as an exhaust for interstellar rockets. It has been known for a long time that very large amounts of energy are needed in order to accelerate a rocket close to the speed of light, if we use any known substance as an exhaust. This is indicated by two equations, which relate the power per unit mass of the rocket, P; the mass of the rocket, M, including the exhaust; the "payload," m, or mass of the rocket without the exhaust; the exhaust velocity as measured in the rocket, V_E; the speed, v, of the rocket when the propellant is used up; and the acceleration, a, of the rocket while it is using its engines,

$$M = m \left(\frac{1+v/c}{1-v/c} \right)^{c/2V_E} , \qquad (3)$$

$$a = \frac{PV_E}{c^2} . \qquad (4)$$

Suppose we wish to make v close to c, which we need for interstellar rocket travel in times within the present human life-span. Then according to the first equation, we must have V_E as large as possible, or else the mass ratio M/m will get very large, which would mean that most of the rocket's mass at takeoff would be propellant. For instance, if we took V_E/c to be 1/10, and wanted v/c to be 1/2, then we would need M/m to be 243, which is unreasonable. Furthermore, if the rocket is to accelerate at 1g until burnout, which is necessary if it is to reach maximum speed within a year or so, then the second equation implies, with $V_E/c=1/10$, a power to mass ratio P of 3×10^8 watts/gm, which also is very hard to achieve. Without tachyons, the best we could do is use photons or neutrinos as an exhaust, which would give $V_E/c=1$, a mass ratio of 1.73 for

$v/c=1/2$, but still require $P=3\times10^7$ watts/gm, which is some 10^{14} times brighter than the sun. In the face of figures such as these, it is not surprising that scientists that have looked into the feasibility of rocket flight at speeds near that of light have concluded that it was forever impossible.

This conclusion can be changed drastically if we are able to use tachyons as an exhaust. We can see from Eqs. (3) and (4) that when V_E/c becomes greater than 1, the mass ratio M/m needed for a given final velocity v gets smaller, and the power output needed for a given acceleration decreases also. If we take the limiting case of an exhaust consisting of infinite speed tachyons, then we find that the mass ratio M/m is 1 for any v less than c, and the needed power output approaches zero for any acceleration we choose. Since this result may seem more magic than physics, it is worthwhile to examine it in more detail. We have seen that, as the speed of a tachyon increases, its energy approaches zero, while its momentum does not approach zero. Now a rocket operates through the reaction to the *momentum* carried away by the exhaust, and its motion is not directly related to the energy carried away. Therefore, tachyons of infinite speed, which carry away momentum but no energy, are an ideal rocket exhaust, as they can propel the rocket without wasting any mass through the energy they carry off. Of course, the ship could be propelled by tachyons of less than infinite speed, but this would be less effective in that it would require a loss of mass or a use of energy. However, any tachyon exhaust would be more effective than any exhaust using ordinary matter.

The above description of the rocket motion is the one that would be given by a passenger in the rocket, for whom the rocket remains at constant speed and constant energy. For a different observer, say one on the earth, the rocket is seen to speed up, and therefore its energy increases. We may then legitimately ask where this energy is coming from. The answer is that the tachyons emitted at infinite speed as seen by the rocket passenger will not be at infinite speed as seen by the earth observer, but rather at some lesser speed, and they will therefore carry both energy and momentum. At first glance, this would seem to make matters even worse, as this energy also must be accounted for. However, as seen from the earth, the tachyons travel toward the rocket rather than away from it. That is, the rocket, which is designed to be a tachyon emitter in its own rest system, will be a tachyon absorber as viewed from earth. Hence the energy needed to accelerate the rocket is obtained from the tachyons absorbed by it. These tachyons are part of the ambient flux mentioned above that interferes with the operation of tachyon communication devices. This shows that the existence of such a flux is a theoretical necessity in order that different observers be able to describe the same phenomenon, the motion of the rocket.

To see what performance characteristics might be built into a tachyon propelled spaceship, let us imagine such a ship weighing 3000 tons, with a thrust of 6 million pounds, both comparable to the values for the existing Saturn V rocket. The ship, propelled by infinite speed tachyons, would have an acceleration of 1g, or about 32 ft/sec^2, again comparable to that of the Saturn V near takeoff. However, unlike the Saturn V, the tachyon propelled ship could carry on this acceleration (as measured by a passenger aboard the ship) indefinitely. As a result, after one year had elapsed on earth, it would be traveling at about .7c. After ten years elapsed on earth, the ship would be almost nine light years from earth, and traveling at .995 of c. In order to stop, say to land on a planet of another star system, the ship would reverse its engines, and the stopping times would be the same as the time for building up maximum speed. These times would all be much smaller when measured by an observer aboard the ship, because of the relativistic time dilatation. Of course, the distances that can be traveled by accelerating continuously at 1g are independent of the method of propulsion. But only by means of tachyon propulsion would it be possible to avoid the overwhelming mass ratios and energy expenditures necessary to continue such an acceleration for the periods needed.

A tachyon propulsion system would require two essential elements. One would be a way of making tachyons in very large quantities from ordinary matter. Perhaps if tachyons exist at all, they can be made, just as all of the unstable particles discovered in recent years can be made, in collisions between the components of ordinary matter. If this can be done, it should be possible to make the very high-speed tachyons needed for most efficient propulsion, as they would not require large amounts of kinetic energy to make them. To get an idea of how many would have to be made, let us use the figures given above of 6 million pounds of thrust. The number of infinite speed tachyons to be expelled per second depends on the value of the mass parameter μ appearing in Eq. (1). If we take μ to be 10^{-24} grams, comparable to its value for known elementary particles such as protons, then we find that it would be necessary to expel 10^{26} tachyons per second from the rocket in order to provide the desired thrust. Assuming that some reaction could be found that produces a tachyon from each reacting proton or neutron, this would require some 100 grams of matter per second to react and produce the necessary tachyons. This figure does not appear to be completely impossible, as the matter would not be used up, but could be used over and over again. What reactions might be used to produce tachyons cannot be determined until tachyons are detected and their interactions with other matter are studied. No energy is needed to produce the tachyons of infinite speed, since their total energy is zero. Some energy could be required if the reaction produces other things as well as tachyons. But there is no reason for this to be the case in all such reactions. Hence we do not expect that there will be any minimum energy requirement for the operation of the tachyon production mechanism.

The other requirement for a tachyon-propelled rocket is some method to direct the tachyons produced out the back of the rocket. If tachyons exist with electric charge, it would be possible to direct them by electromagnetic fields and steer them out the back in that way. However, there is some experimental evidence indicating that charged tachyons probably do not exist.[4] If only neutral tachyons can be produced, other methods must be found to direct them. One such method could be the following. If tachyons are made by objects that are at rest, they will emerge in a random distribution, with equal numbers forward and backward. However, if the source of the tachyons is in motion in some direction, then on the average more tachyons will go in that direction than in the opposite direction. Hence if we can get a flow of ordinary matter toward the back of the rocket, which is not difficult to achieve, the tachyons produced by this matter would tend to go in this direction, rather than the other. This is sufficient to give propulsion, which requires only that more momentum be carried away in one direction than in the other.

Hence it would appear to me that if tachyons interact with ordinary matter at all, which is another way of saying that they exist, then it should at least theoretically be possible to propel spaceships by producing and ejecting tachyons. If this could be done practically, it would open up the road to interstellar travel at near light speeds, a road which otherwise might be always closed to us. While this is not the only way in which interstellar travel could be practiced, it would involve a relatively small change in the cultural patterns that have been followed heretofore in earthly explorations, as compared to other proposed methods.[5] Therefore, even if we are able to find other biological or sociological solutions to the equation time equals distance over speed, tachyon-propelled rockets would, if they can be constructed, play an important role in exploring the stars.

One final note of caution must be inserted. These considerations remain as purely hypothetical as the existence of tachyons. The latter is not required by physical theory, but simply is permitted by it. The same is true of all other forms of matter known to us. We have no theories that specify what forms of matter *do* exist, but only theories that enable us to describe the forms of matter we discover. The only arbiter for existence in contemporary physics is an experimental search. Perhaps at some future time this will change, and theoretical physics will be able to predict from basic principles what types of elementary particles do exist, just as it is now able to predict which chemical elements do exist. When that day arrives, we shall be able to determine also whether tachyons exist. It is possible that a future theory of particles would give some clue about how to synthesize types that do not occur naturally, just as we have been able to do with certain of the chemical elements. In that case, we could hope to manufacture tachyons by specifically designed reactions, rather than hoping they are produced occasionally. Such a development would make the use of tachyons along lines outlined here much more straightforward and feasible.

REFERENCES

1. G. Feinberg, *Physical Review*, 159, 1089, 1967. O. M. P. Bilaniuk *et al.*, *American Journal of Physics*, 30, 718, 1962.
2. T. Alvager and M. Kreisler, *Physical Review*, 171, 1357, 1968. C. Baltay *et al.*, *Physical Review*, Vol. 1, No. 3, Feb. 1, 1970.
3. See, for example, S. van Hoerner in *Science*, 137, 18, 1962.
4. Alvager and Kreisler, op. cit.
5. For example, F. Dyson in *Physics Today*, October 1968, p. 41.

D. M. COLE *and* D. W. COX

Inside-out Worlds

The following article by Dandridge Cole and Donald Cox is an excerpt from their book Islands in Space. *The islands to which they were referring are the asteroids, the chunks of matter circling the sun beyond the orbit of Mars. The largest of these is less than five hundred miles in diameter and the smallest has undoubtedly not yet been discovered. Cole and Cox suggest converting one of the larger of these planetoids into a thin shelled "bubble" which would serve as a space colony for several hundred thousand inhabitants. By controlling the rotation rate and admission of sunlight to the core of the sphere, the environment could be precisely tailored. Until his untimely death, Dandridge Cole was a space program analyst for the General Electric Company; Donald Cox is a lecturer and writer on space and the technological future. They have described an engineering project for the next century.*

The occupation of the planetoids will probably take place in phases, beginning with the landing of the first explorers who will use their spaceships as their living quarters.

Next a temporary small base might be established, using empty propellant tanks, possibly covered with loose rubble from the planetoid. The purpose of the temporary base would be primarily for exploration, prospecting, scientific studies, etc.

In the third phase of planetoid occupancy, men would begin to make practical use of the planetoid resources for propellants and supplies, and for valuable metals to ship back to the Earth. In pursuing these mining operations, large caverns would be cut out of the planetoids which could be converted into living quarters.

This possibility of hollowing out planetoids for space colonies was discussed some years ago by L. R. Shepard, I. M. Levitt, and other scientists and science fiction writers. It is believed that the first discussion of this possibility was by Dr. J. D. Bernal in his book *The World, the Flesh and the Devil.*

Gradually, over the course of many years, a major fraction of the material of the planetoid would be processed and redistributed. This could lead to a great expansion in the size of the planetoid as materials were carried outward and great empty spaces were created. Eventually, caverns extending for miles would take up the entire inside of the enlarged cosmic body and the colonists would have built themselves a new world.

While the first planetoid worlds will probably be hollowed out over a long period, the cosmic engineers and colonists of the more distant future might become impatient with such a slow process.

When large-scale operations in space have become relatively commonplace, engineers will begin to think of ways of creating large habitable planetoid worlds in one process. They may consider taking an iron planetoid, melting it, blowing it up into a long cylindrical bubble, and then waiting for the iron to solidify and cool down to a temperature consistent with human habitation. Such a project would dwarf anything ever undertaken on the Earth. How could engineers possibly bring it about even with the techniques and machines of the future?

It would be foolish to try to specify exactly how an operation of this magnitude would be conducted perhaps fifty years from now, because of new scientific and engineering discoveries which will be made in the meantime. However, we might be able to suggest some general techniques that could be used.

John Campbell has suggested constructing large curved mirrors in space, and using concentrated solar heat for melting, cutting, and shaping planetoid materials. One of the authors also suggested that giant solar mirrors could be used for forming the planetoid bubbles.[1]

The first step for the world makers would be construction of the giant mirror which might measure several miles in diameter. Formed under zero gravity conditions, it could be of very light construction with the mirror surface itself of light, silvered plastic similar to that of the Echo balloon satellites.

The first job for the mirror would be to bore one or more holes down near the center of the planetoid. Ideally, an elongated planetoid would be selected, perhaps one mile in diameter and two miles long. The holes would be bored down to the center line or long axis and when completed, would be charged with tanks of water.

The planetoid would then be set spinning slowly, such that the entire body would be bathed in the intense heat of the reflected and concentrated sunlight. Gradually the flying iron mountain would be heated to the melting point all over its surface, and slowly the heat would creep inward until almost the whole object was molten.

When the entire body was melted, the gravitational and cohesive forces would presumably pull it into a spherical shape. This would not be desirable, as we will see later, and would not occur if the engineers had done their job. The central axis of the planetoid would be the last part to melt. As long as this remained solid, the melting body would hold a cylindrical rather than spherical shape. Thus the engineers would design the water tanks to explode from internal steam pressure just as the central axis melted. Then the released expanding steam would blow up the planetoid into an iron balloon some ten miles in diameter and twenty miles long.

When the hollow shell had solidified and cooled off, the construction crews would affix the giant mirror to one end and direct a beam of reflected light down the long axis of the cylinder to form a linear sun.

The next jobs would be to set up plants for manufacturing air, water, soil, etc. for the new world. Raw materials would probably be obtained from a rock planetoid which had been captured and pulled alongside.

Gravity for the new world could be supplied to the extent desired by spinning the planetoid about its long axis. This would produce a centrifugal force which would seem to push objects against the outer wall. The advantage of a cylindrical as compared to a spherical shape should be obvious because of the larger surface area available with the desired artificial gravity.

Suppose, for example, that the inhabitants elected to have a gravity equal to one fifth of the normal surface gravity of the Earth (such that a two-hundred-pound man would weigh only forty pounds). To produce this effect in a cylinder ten miles in diameter, it would be necessary to give the planetoid a spin rate of nine revolutions per hour or a "day" of 6.6 minutes. At this rate, the circumference would be moving at 200 feet per second (compared to the Earth's equatorial spin rate of 1.5 thousand feet per second), but people inside would not be aware of this motion. They would only sense the apparent gravitational force caused by the rotation. In addition, people or objects in motion would experience a second apparent force called the "coriolis force" which appears to deflect the path of moving objects.

If someone standing on the inner wall of the spinning cylinder tried to throw a ball straight toward the center, they would find that it would be deflected away from a straight line on a curved path in the direction of rotation. If we say that the cylinder is turning toward the east, then balls thrown straight upward would be deflected toward the east. On the other hand, a ball dropped from a height would not fall straight down but would be deflected toward the west.

To a person raised inside this strange world who was never

told of its spinning motion, both the centrifugal and the coriolis forces would be as mysterious and unexplainable as gravity is to us. However, if the person happened to be a physicist, he could eventually figure out that his world was turning, and even calculate the spin rate. Some scientists believe that our own gravity is just the result of some strange curved motion of the universe that we will probably never be able to visualize.

The gravity of the tiny inside-out world would decrease from one fifth Earth normal at the cylindrical surface to zero at the central axis and at the poles at the ends of the central axis. Thus a two-hundred-pound man who traveled from the equator to one of the poles would find that his weight dropped from forty pounds to zero during the process.

The inside-out world has a slight built-in equatorial bulge such that the equator is always downhill. Thus, water from the melting pole caps would flow downhill by rivers and streams to the central equatorial sea.

The low temperature of the poles would be maintained by great disk-shaped shades near the ends of the central sun which would keep the poles in perpetual darkness. Also, thermal radiators would be mounted outside the planetoid at both ends to reject heat and balance the continual influx of heat from the mirror.

Water vapor which evaporated from the rivers and the sea would tend to condense and freeze at the poles. As the mass of ice and snow piled up, it would tend to slide downhill into the unshaded sunlight, whence it would melt and run back to the sea.

The central beam of sunlight itself would probably shine down through a transparent and hollow tube. The tube would be filled with a gas of the required composition and density to produce the desired scattered and fluorescent light and heat. The "sun" could be turned off at intervals by blocking the mirror if periods of nighttime were desired.

Soil for the inside surface would be made from pulverized rock and the decayed remains of several cover crops. A parklike or more natural appearing random countryside would be land-scaped to suit the desires of the colonists.

The ten-mile-diameter cylinder world would have an inside surface area of 628 square miles, over half the size of the state of Rhode Island. Uncrowded Rhode Island has a population of 800 thousand people. Our inside-out world could very com-fortably hold perhaps 100 thousand people. If the average in-habitant paid twenty thousand dollars for his land, two billion dollars would be available for construction of the new world in space.

Of course, the many important uses for a planetoid colony would probably attract considerable government support and it would not be necessary for the colonists to fund the entire project.

Men of the modern world do not dream of paradise as much as did their ancestors of even the last century. Of course, the underprivileged dream of wealth and enjoying the luxuries of the more fortunate. But the race as a whole does not dream so much of presently unattainable wealth, comfort, pleasure, etc.

Perhaps this is because we already have so much—as a race—perhaps because we realize that material welfare alone will not bring happiness, and perhaps because we are beginning to realize that we actually can accomplish almost anything con-ceivable of a material nature that we decide is really worthwhile.

But there may still be some who dream of a physical paradise and for them, and for all the dreamers of the past, the hollow planetoid would be heaven.

Within the inside-out world, all the physical conditions of the environment would be completely under the control of the in-habitants. The temperature, air pressure, humidity, oxygen con-tent, pollen content, rainfall, snowfall, day-night cycle, etc. would all be under complete control. The quality and quantity of food produced, the number and type of trees, shrubs, flowers, and streams; the wildlife, birds, fish, etc. would all be as de-sired. There would be no harmful microorganisms or insects, but only those needed to maintain the balanced ecology. There would be no pollution of the air or water since all biological and chemical wastes would require reprocessing in any case and there would be no point in dumping them into the gas and liquid reservoirs.

Very little physical labor would be required since all routine tasks would be done with automated machinery. This would apply also to routine clerical and mental work, such that drudgery would be almost completely eliminated.

The control over the environment of this Utopia would be so great that the inhabitants could even control the force of gravity for their world. If they wanted a full Earth gravity, they could have it. If they wanted their weights to be one fifth or one tenth of Earth normal, they could arrange that also. Or they could cut the force of gravity down one hundred or one thousand times below Earth normal, and could even change it back and forth from time to time.

One of the commonest types of sleeping dreams is that of flying freely through the air using only our own arms for propulsion and support. This dream is probably as old as the race of men and perhaps even older, for even the pre-men probably dreamed. Our present ability to fly through the air with high-powered mechanical contrivances does not satisfy this universal desire for freedom from the force of gravity.

One who believed in prophetic dreams might argue that we have actually foreseen the future existence of these low-gravity hollow worlds in our dreams of powerless and almost gravity-less flight; because we know of no other way in which these dreams could ever be satisfied.

Imagine for a moment that you live in this hollow world in a little house in the country and that the spin rate has been set to produce one tenth of Earth normal gravity. You decide to go for a short fly and a breath of country air.

You put on your flying suit with the paddlelike wings attached to the sleeves and extending about two feet beyond your hands, and the light cloth sail extending between arms and legs.

You give a slight push, glide across the house and out through the front door, folding your wings momentarily to make your exit. Outside you land on your front lawn and get set for your take-off spring.

Since you are fairly athletic and have strong legs, you shoot straight up with wings closed to a height of thirty feet. (On Earth you could raise the center of gravity of your body three feet straight up, which is rather good.)

At thirty feet, high over the top of your house, you come to a stop and maintain your altitude by flapping your wings. This is not difficult since you have a mass of 160 pounds and a weight of only sixteen pounds, no more than a small turkey. Thus, you need support only eight pounds on each arm and this is no strain even for someone who is not in top physical condition.

You look around briefly at the rolling hills, the green forests and the open meadows of your homeland and then drop into a steep glide down the valley. The dive brings you speed which you would lose again as you pull up to recapture your altitude, but this time you flap your wings vigorously and ascend to some seventy feet before resting in a longer but slower glide.

In passing the stream at the lower end of the valley, you spot a trout just breaking water and throw yourself into a steep dive. You make a playful try at catching the fish who has risen over ten feet out of the water, but you misjudge the correction for the coriolis force and pass to one side.

But now you are heading for the stream at high speed and with considerable momentum. Your small wings are not sufficient for a sharp turn and you end up ingloriously in the trout stream producing a splash of water rising thirty or forty feet.

While this unauspicious beginning of your outing dampens your clothing, it does not dampen your spirit and you spring into the air with new energy. Cold and wet and a bit angry, you start out to set your own personal altitude record.

Flying straight up is really no harder for an experienced flyer than brisk walking on Earth and after a half hour of steady flying you have risen to a height of some two and a half miles. Halfway to the central sun of your world you find the flying much easier since your weight has been reduced to only eight pounds, but it is also becoming uncomfortably warm. Remembering the experience of Icarus who flew too close to the sun and melted his wings, you decide to forego any further conquest of altitude and settle for lazy contemplation of the beautiful scenery on your gentle glide back to the ground.

From this height you can get a much better impression of your cylindrical world than from down on the ground. Through the clear air you can easily see the pole cap about five miles to the north and the equatorial sea almost an equal distance to the south. In fact, you can get a view of the entire world-circling equatorial sea and even make out the boats on the far side sailing upside down across your sky.

The upcurving and encircling horizon is not disturbing to you, a native of the inside-out world, and even visitors from Earth quickly lose their concern. They soon realize that the ships, vehicles, people, houses, etc. that they can clearly see through binoculars above them on the opposite side of the world are not going to fall on them. Afterward they gradually adjust to the upcurving horizon and begin to enjoy the greatly expanded view of the scenery that this affords. Any small hill in the hollow world gives the sightseer a broader panorama of forests, hills, meadows, villages, lakes, etc., than even a view from a high mountain on the Earth.

So you drift slowly back toward your home with your clothing well dried by your close approach to the sun and a great feeling of peace and contentment with your happy, worry-free life in this Utopian world. Your exercise has stimulated your appetite and you speculate idly on what selections you will make from your food-o-mat for the evening meal. After supper, of course, you must attend the village meeting to settle that aggravating question of whether to have rain once or twice a week during the next three months.

And, of course, that is the other side of the coin that the dreamer sometimes fails to see. We *can* have a physical paradise with the whole of our environment controlled exactly as we wish. But what do we wish and what do our neighbors wish and will our wishes be the same as theirs? Power brings responsibility and the necessity for making decisions about everything within your sphere of power. If you have complete control over your physical environment, you also have complete responsibility.

The inhabitants of the hollow planetoid will have a physical paradise to the extent that they really know what they want as individuals and can agree as a group. And that brings us to the much more important question of the social and political life of the planetoid world and the advantages or disadvantages of such an existence as compared to our own.

The planetoid colony would necessarily be highly organized, with the cooperation, specialization, and interdependence of the inhabitants approaching that of the cells of the human body. The happiness and safety of the colonists would depend almost entirely on the degree to which they could achieve this social harmony. This is, of course, true on the Earth also, but not to the same extent. The closed-cycle society would be far more sensitive to aberrant, anti-social, and destructive behavior.

Because of these requirements for a highly disciplined society, some people have concluded that the space colony would necessarily have a totalitarian government—a 1984 "Big Brother" society complete with brainwashing, secret police, etc. According to this theory, people would be forced into their tiny compartments of unrewarding routine work with any deviations severely punished. However, this does not seem reasonable or probable. While some misguided governments or groups might try to set up such a colony, it is doubtful that it could succeed for long. Like all the rigid totalitarian regimes of the past, it would contain the seeds of its own destruction. Since men naturally resist compulsion, forced cooperation cannot be as productive as free cooperation. Also, the creative talents of the workers are stifled if forced to conform to the rigid plan of the government. But the most serious defect is the inherent instability of such a system.

Compulsory conformity cannot be effective unless erected on a basis of physical compulsion. But this implies the possibility of physical resistance or violent rebellion. But violent conflict within a delicately balanced closed-cycle system would be catastrophic.

While the necessity for specialization might suggest a workman doomed to a life of routine drudgery, such a situation would be unlikely. Routine work of all types would be handled by machines, and it would be primarily creative work which would be performed by the human inhabitants. Men are basically independent and creative when not overwhelmed by group pressures to conform, and it would be their creative talents which would be needed in such professions as teaching, law, medicine, science, engineering, architecture, music, painting, writing, landscaping, military, statecraft, entertainment, etc. For the skilled but less creative there would be ample work in maintenance, repair, service, distribution of goods, etc.

There would be a much greater demand for teachers in such a society and also for members of the other professions. The greater material wealth of the society would be channeled into a higher percentage of doctors, lawyers, teachers, scientists, etc., reaching perhaps three to four times the per cent in the United States of the 1960s. Thus, there would be one teacher for each ten students rather than for thirty or forty students and the level of education would be raised enormously. Likewise, the teachers would be freed from all routine tasks by machines and would be able to concentrate their time and energy on more important questions of how to communicate new concepts, how to motivate, etc.

While it would be necessary to invoke a rigid discipline in times of emergency, full political freedom would be the rule. If men cannot express their opinions and air their differences in both verbal and written form, the bottled up resentments will eventually explode in violent rebellion.

The latest discoveries in semantics, game theory, the psychology of personality, of motivation, and of optimized positive behavior would, of course, be available to the highly trained teachers of the new world. And the students would have been raised from birth in an environment of consistent, affectionate discipline with an optimum balance of freedom and direction. Thus, they would be emotionally equipped to respond vigorously, positively, and confidently to new learning experiences, and would learn rapidly and well.

The new world society, like any society, would have to be democratic to be stable. And stability would be essential for the safety of the whole society. And of course, a pure democracy with decisions reached through simple majority vote, would not be adequate or stable. Representative government would be necessary as would constitutional protection of minority rights.

In short, it would appear that the carefully balanced closed-cycle society would not necessarily be totalitarian and would, in fact, more probably have a government generally approximating those of the Western democracies. While it would be necessary to have a strong executive office and strict military regulations pertaining to some critical functions and situations, it would also be necessary to insure the individual political freedom and civil liberties. We have found in the West that these things need not be incompatible.

In summary then, we can ask the question—what would be the purpose in setting up a colony in a hollow planetoid? One way to answer this question is to ask another—how would we describe man's age-old dream of heaven or Utopia? The dream worlds of heaven or Utopia which have fascinated men since the dawn of history have two basic characteristics—one involving the physical environment and the other involving man's own nature. Political and social theories, psychological and theological theories, and basic questions regarding man's real nature and his capacity for growth and improvement, all these are involved in our speculations regarding the perfect world or perfect society. And the setting for our Utopia would not affect these things directly, although there could be important secondary effects. But, physically, life on the captured planetoid could approximate closely our fondest dreams of paradise.

Large chambers hollowed out of the inside of the captured satellite and possibly occupying the whole interior could be landscaped to form a pleasant "natural" countryside of hills and valleys, forests, and meadows, lakes and streams. And all of our new knowledge of emotions, behavior, communication, etc. could be employed to make life in such a society productive and happy.

And would this new world really be inside-out or perverse? Or is it perhaps our own Earth, with its external life (on the outer surface of the planet) that really has its insides out?

REFERENCE

1. D. M. Cole, "Extraterrestrial Colonies," *Journal of the Institute of Navigation*, Summer-Autumn, Vol. 7, Nos. 2 and 3, 1960.

5

A. G. WILSON *and*

T. J. GORDON

Requirements for Communications to a Naive Recipient

The following article by astronomer and logician Dr. A. G. Wilson and engineer T. J. Gordon deals with the possibility of communicating with other forms of intelligent life. Many scientists believe that communicative societies exist elsewhere in the universe; in fact, Dr. Frank Drake has estimated that between a thousand and a million such societies exist within a thousand light years of the earth. Yet why haven't we heard them? New sensitive radio telescopes all over the world are continually listening in in almost all parts of the radio and microwave spectrum. Wilson and Gordon suggest we may not have detected intelligent signals because adequate decoding keys do not yet exist.

Previous authors have invented various kinds of languages which they believed other races might use in trying to contact us. For the most part these have assumed that evolution brought the distant being along biological paths at least grossly similar to our own. But perhaps it is only our supreme egotism which leads us to believe that intelligent beings on other planets in distant galaxies think, sense, and reason as we do. Differences in thought and sensory processes will lead to great difficulties in establishing communications between interstellar races (or between any races, for that matter). The coding of a message sent by an intelligent race to attract the attention of another race therefore will have to be very carefully designed. Wilson and Gordon suggest some new criteria for this language.

Because transmissions from pulsars have many of the characteristics of artificial signals, Wilson and Gordon illustrate their concepts by analyzing the signals of C.P. 1919. They say, as do most scientists, that these signals are almost certainly of natural origin. Yet they find a translation key: The symbol 4pi. A coincidence? Most probably.

INTRODUCTION

Shannon and others, in developing information theory, have dealt with the problem of communications between parties who understand the nature of the information flowing in the data channel between them. This understanding permits a translation from the signal, whatever its form, to a language understandable by the receiver. The problem of information exchange becomes considerably more complex if the receiver does not have the code which permits him to convert the signals generated by the sender to a language understandable to him. Without the dictionary which permits translation from transmitted signals to the receiver's language, information theory is compounded by cryptographic difficulties. The present paper deals with the problem of transmitting information to a receiver who does not possess decoding keys. This situation arises in teaching a student a new language, in attempted communication between alien species, and is in a sense the problem at the basis of all education. The problem we have posed is the inverse of the process of encoding messages for security. In the security situation, the sender purposely garbles his information in a way which he hopes will confuse an unintended recipient. We ask how a sender might choose to encode his information so that recipients may have the *least* difficulty in decoding.

Several investigators in the disciplines of education, cryptography, psychology, and exobiology have addressed certain aspects of this problem. For example, Hans Freudenthal in his book *Lincos: Design of a Language for Cosmic Intercourse* proposed a "lingua cosmica" in which instruction was based on mathematical relationships.[1] F. Drake, B. M. Oliver, and C. Sagan have proposed televisionlike codes by which the information is transmitted from one extraterrestrial species to another through the use of digital codes easily converted to simple pictures; these pictures would convey information designed to build a decoding language.[2] These diverse suggestions have incorporated ingenious coding systems but have relied on the supposedly superior intelligence of the sender and the enlightened insight of the naive recipient. We hope to approach the problem in a more systematic way so that general rules for encoding information for a naive recipient can be developed. Ideally these rules would lead to the definition of patterns of encoding and transmission which permit unknown and untutored recipients to reach an understanding of the information being transmitted in the shortest possible time.

INTELLECTUAL MATCHING

Data transmitted in a communication link is information only if the receiver can understand it. As the communication link imposes certain physical requirements on the transmitter and receiver, the conversion of information to data and back to information requires an intellectual match of sorts between the originator and recipient. The greater the precision of this match the easier it will be to reach understanding. If the mismatch is too great, communication will be difficult or impossible. It is somewhat like the electrical analogue for maximum power transfer which occurs when two electrical circuits are matched in impedance. We do not yet understand fully the elements of intellectual match, but certain aspects of it are apparent. Besides being in the right place at the right time, a naive recipient must somehow share with the sender: modes of sensation; a body of previous experience; the intent to communicate and understand; concepts of structure and process including time, order, and interval; and, finally, technology. It is probably not necessary for all of these factors to be present at one time in any given knowledge transfer situation; however, if they are present, there will likely be an "information resonance" which will improve the efficiency with which a naive recipient can reach an understanding of the data being transmitted in a strange communication link. These elements apply to teaching situations whether they occur in a classroom, between adult and teen-ager, missionary and aborigine, or between interstellar civilizations.

THE REQUIREMENTS FOR SHARING MODES OF SENSATION

Words of a language are symbols for things, experiences, or ideas. Communication (i.e., successful transmission and reception of ideas) is probably most easily initiated if props can be used that illustrate the physical reality which the words of the new language represent. A teacher might point to something and then draw the sign or speak the word that represents the item. Children are taught new languages this way; cryptographers decode obscure texts by searching for repetitive phrases or key words that serve as conceptual referents for them.

However, if knowledge of the object or idea is gained by the sender through a sensing mode not shared by the recipient, it will be difficult to convey information about the sensation through a data link. How can a person describe the feeling of "red" to another person who has been color-blind since birth? It is possible that other groups are receptive to excitations that we cannot appreciate. For example, other species might be sensitive to certain ESP modes or might "see" in the X-ray or radio frequency ranges. Information explainable only in terms of "sender unique" sensations is not well suited for the establishment of codes translatable by naive recipients.

But irrespective of the frequency ranges and modes of sensation, the originator must convert sensation to knowledge and knowledge to data which is encoded into the information channel. This channel makes the data accessible to recipients possessing receivers that can intercept it. It becomes information if they can translate it. This process of translation into and out of a commonly accessible channel can permit species of vastly different sensory capabilities to communicate with each other. A planet of blind men might send by radio that which they hear and a planet of deaf men might understand this information by viewing it on a television receiver. One is reminded of the methods used by Anne Sullivan in teaching Helen Keller. Here the shared sensation was touch, and all referents were converted to that sensation.

Thus, sensation match requires a sensation overlap sufficient for a common information channel to be established which is either directly or through instruments accessible to the senders' and recipients' capabilities. Once the channel is established, differences between sensory capacities of sender and receiver can probably be overcome.

PREVIOUS EXPERIENCE MATCH

When two species attempt communication there must be some common experience between them. In order to establish referents for the code both species must have some knowledge of the referent. A sender, for example, could use a rock as the first key of a code dictionary only for a naive receiver who lived on a planet that also had rocks. But not only must the "things" of experience be available to both sender and receiver, but also a similar way of processing experience. Primitive peoples shown two-dimensional drawings or photographs for the first time perceive them only as masses of varying densities of white, black, and gray. Their processing of experience does not permit them to understand the meaning of the two-dimensional analogue of three-dimensional objects. Only through specialized processing of experience does the relationship between the physical three-dimensional thing and its two-dimensional metaphor become apparent.[3]

Thus, the concept of experience overlap requires that senders or teachers seek initial referents and processes that are within the experience of their students.

INTENT TO COMMUNICATE AND UNDERSTAND

As the desire to learn motivates students, the desire to understand the code must motivate the naive recipient. If the recipient has no intent to decode, the sender's schemes can be as ingenious as possible to no avail. Since intent can be fleeting, the sender wishing to establish a channel of information flow should probably use the simplest keys and include a reward stimulus in which the recipient is continually encouraged to learn the code to increasing depths of sophistication.

Of course, this mechanism would have to be built into the signal. One can imagine a signal which has a number of built-in markers, the first of which is relatively crude, indicating simply that the signal is of intelligent origin. Once discovered, this first marker might serve as the initial deciphering key to somewhat more subtle information contained in the signal. This second level of information might provide insight to a more complex decoding scheme, so that at each step discovery of the code would be the reward. However, it should be recognized that supposition of this type of structure presumes that the species share psychological mechanisms which provide pleasure from discovery—a puzzle-solving propensity.

THE PHYSIOLOGICAL MATCH OF TIME, ORDER, AND INTERVAL

Is it necessary that our characteristic time for detection of change be shared by other species? Even though information density is clearly a function of channel bandwidth, a long-lived species might transmit their referents over very long periods of time unacceptable to short-lived groups in terms of their attention span. Similarly, if the short-lived group is the sender the long-lived group might overlook codes not commensurate with their temporal patterns of behavior.

Imagine a race of intelligent individuals with life-spans equivalent to one thousand of our years. They might well presume that other races would easily detect a key transmitted over a period equivalent to an earth month. But another race which flourished for a day would sense the key only as another slowly changing aspect of nature. Furthermore, it may not be necessary that diverse species think in terms of the same kind of sequential order as we. To us it is natural to think in terms of processes flowing from beginnings to ends; perhaps other types of intelligence move from the center out in Gaussian thought patterns. Thus, a potential sender should seek to confine the code to a time span of interest to his receiver and transmit it in such a way that his receiver is likely to understand its order and sequence.

TECHNOLOGY MATCH

Aside from overlapping psychological, physiological, and physical characteristics, the communicating species, if located remotely from one another, would have to share technology. It would be futile for one race to signal with lasers, for example, while the other was searching with radio receivers. We have no way of knowing whether our technological evolution is typical, and the small amount of evidence available is inconclusive. Races that may have developed in relative isolation, the Egyptians and the Mayans, for example, both had calendars, but one employed the wheel and the other did not. Is it reasonable to guess that in the course of scientific and technological evolution optical technology precedes radio technology, radio precedes microwave, and microwave precedes coherent light physics?

SPACE-TIME MATCH

It goes almost without saying that for two races to communicate they must exist at proper space-time separation. If a race ten thousand years away were to begin signaling us today, their discovery would have to wait ten thousand years since there is apparently no signaling mechanism that can exceed the speed of light. The word "apparently" is used since clearly we have not explored all possible signaling mechanisms; in fact, only two or three have been suggested so far. These include the use of electromagnetic radiations and the use of physical artifacts to mark actual visits. That other devices will be discovered is almost certain. For example, faster-than-light particles, tachyons, have been described theoretically; can communication systems be designed around them or do there exist ESP channels whose relation to space-time manifolds results in "instantaneous communication"?

CODING CONCEPTS

The foregoing discussion suggests several rules that a sender might follow in order to maximize the opportunity for a naive recipient to understand his attempts at transmitting a language code:

1. Transmit on channels on which the recipient is likely to possess a sensitive receiver.
2. Avoid the use of reference to sensations not likely to be shared by the receiver.

3. Use referents that are likely to be known by the receiver, using props to establish semantic referents whenever possible.

4. Transmit in a way that provides reinforcement, reward, and encouragement for the discovery of the translation key to enhance the receiver's intent to learn.

5. Keep the duration of transmission within a time period reasonable for likely receivers.

6. Use a code that is unambiguous with respect to order or sequence.

7. Use as primitive a technology as possible.

8. Keep up efforts to communicate over as long a period as possible.

If we apply these rules to the case of attempted interstellar communication from one species to another, we can make several generalizations about the form in which these transmissions might occur.

There are at least three ways in which a naive recipient might become aware of communications from an interstellar civilization. First, he might intercept a message specifically designed to initiate communication between the sender and other species. This would be most fortunate since this type of transmission would probably include simple keys to the code being used by the sender. Second, as pointed out by several researchers, he might overhear on-going conversations between species who already know the code. Third, the receiver might overhear operational procedures such as navigational beacons (we use loran and Transit satellites to aid navigation on the earth) or scientific experiments related to the space surrounding the sender's planet (we have radar-mapped the moon, Venus, and Mars). With this sort of signal the naive receiver probably would be forced to infer the nature of the operation before any information could be obtained from the data he received.

SELECTION OF REFERENTS

In the simplest case, where the sender is trying to attract attention and convey a simple code to naive recipients, concepts of shared technology, sensation, and experience would be used to fit as wide a potential audience as possible. What referents might the sender choose to establish his code? Certain universal physical and mathematical constants immediately come to mind such as the mass of a hydrogen nucleus, the velocity of light, the fine structure constant, pi, and so forth. If the prop selected as a referent is a physical constant it should be in non-dimensional form or in units based on universal constants. Physical constants such as the mass of the hydrogen nucleus or the speed of light would be difficult to encode in a sufficiently general form but constants such as the fine structure constant or pi fulfill this criterion. In addition, no matter what the referent, the numbering system used by the sender must be sufficiently general that it is likely to lie within the experience of the receiver.

The sender might choose to use a natural law as a referent. Typically, he might select one of the laws of planetary motion, radioactive decay, black body radiation, gas laws, parity, etc. Here it is the form which is important. Kepler's third law of planetary motion could be represented as $K = \dfrac{D^3}{T^2}$ and intensity of radiation as $R = \dfrac{K}{D^2}$. However, these forms might be subject to ambiguous interpretation. For example, $R = \dfrac{K}{D^2}$ is not only the form of the equation for radiation density, it serves as the equation for the area of a circle as well. Implicit in the use of natural laws as referents is the concept of "equivalence" which a sender would probably wish to establish first if he were to use this approach.

The sender might choose to use another class of concepts as his semantic referent: natural processes. He might choose to illustrate his key by demonstrating counting systems or illustrating fission or fusion or number sets.

A sender in selecting from among these potential referents would have to judge a priori what the recipient would likely know. He might reason that any listener capable of intercepting his signal would have to have certain knowledge and he might base his selection of the referent on this knowledge. For example, if information were being transmitted on a radio frequency he might select a referent associated with knowledge required in the construction of radio receivers or with the physics of electromagnetic radiation. Thus, the question resolves to: What referent is unitless, baseless, unambiguous, unnatural, transmittable within a time span reasonable to likely receivers and associated with the knowledge likely to be held by a culture capable of building the required receiver?

IDENTIFYING ARTIFICIAL SOURCES

The problem in differentiating between natural phenomena and artificial phenomena is not trivial. By no means do we have a complete catalogue of natural phenomena and processes; hence it is difficult to categorize new observations. We can say that an artificial signal would be likely to have the following attributes:

1. It would not match previously known natural phenomena.
2. It would require an explanation of great complexity in terms of natural processes.
3. It would be clearly distinguishable from noise.

The fact that its explanation by artificial means might require the postulation of a technology beyond our own existing or projected capabilities would not rule out its artificial origin since clearly the originator might be using processes beyond our imagination.

AN ILLUSIVE EXAMPLE OF DECODING

Today with some fifty pulsars having been discovered and with their properties fairly well observed, it is highly likely that pulsars are properly identified with an unobserved species of star that was first predicted in 1938—the *neutron star*. Although there does not yet exist a completely satisfactory model for pulsar behavior, the neutron star model is the only one that comes close to furnishing a theoretical base for the observations. However, shortly after pulsars were first discovered their then observed properties satisfied many of the criteria which potentially distinguish artificial from natural signals. Pulsars did not match any previously known natural phenomena, there were no good natural models, and their signals were clearly not noise. Specifically what was intriguing was that their pulse signals were precisely periodic and possessed a fine, accurately positioned substructure that varied in amplitude pulse to pulse. This same description applies to our own pulse code telemetry systems and is largely consistent with our ideas about how to place information on an electromagnetic carrier.

As an exercise to develop the ideas implicit in the detection, recognition, and decoding of possible signals of an extraterrestrial intelligence the authors in the summer of 1968 began an investigation of the signal characteristics of the pulsars that had been discovered up to that time and, in particular, C.P. 1919. This work was begun not as pulsar research per se, but because of the first order similarity between pulsar signals and the expected forms of signals of intelligent origin as research to explore the epistemological difficulties implicit in non-natural signal recognition, and in support of our interest in studying means of communication that might be open between alien species.

The generalized form of the signals from C.P. 1919 is shown below:

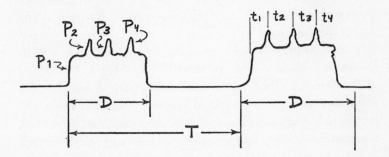

In all pulsars, the major pulses P_1 occur at very precise time intervals, T. Typically, this interval is between .25 and 2 seconds for known pulsars, and can be measured in many cases to nine significant figures. The major pulses, P_1, last for a duration, D, which can be measured much less precisely, but is of the order of tens of milliseconds. In the case of pulsar C.P. 1919, Drake[4] reported the existence of three subpulses, P_2, P_3, and P_4, that vary from major pulse to major pulse. The pulse height of P_1 also varies, but over a much longer time interval.

Taking the viewpoint of the cryptanalyst rather than the astrophysicist, the variable parameters of this signal format (that is, the variables that would contain information if the signal were of intelligent origin) are the heights of the pulses P_1, P_2, P_3, and P_4.

In searching for a possible key, we found that for pulsars C.P. 1919, C.P. 0834, C.P. 0950, and C.P. 1133:

$$(1) \quad \frac{D^2}{T} = A$$

where A is essentially the same constant for all the pulsars and equals about 1 millisecond. (This same relation does not appear to hold for all the newly discovered pulsars.)

As a decoding step, this equation might be rewritten as:

$$(2) \quad D^2 = (0.1)^3 \, T$$

which suggests the form, but not the content, of Kepler's third law. However, it is very unlikely that this specific relation could be a "message," since it implies an extremely improbable coincidence of number bases and time units between the transmitting society and our own.

In addition to units and base of number systems other complications immediately come to mind. First, there is the matter of the Doppler effect which will modify both T and D. If a pulsar lies within a few hundred parsecs,[5] and its velocity with respect to the sun is similar to that of stars in this neighborhood, it would be moving with a velocity of the order of 30 km/sec.

or less. This gives rise to a change in A of only one part in 10^4. Thus, unless the pulsars are moving rapidly, we can still say D^2/T is a constant close in value to one millisecond.

The presence of the dimension of seconds (a social unit of earth's civilizations) in Equation (1) essentially eliminates A from our consideration as a translating key. Ideally this key should be dimensionless, easily recognizable, and simple to use in later translations. In order to non-dimensionalize the time base of the signals, we would have to divide each interval by some time unit known both to us and the supposedly transmitting society. We considered using some universally available period of time such as the orbital period of a hydrogen electron or $\sqrt{Gh/c^5}$, but then it struck us that the signal itself might contain the proper time base. For C.P. 1919:

$$(3) \quad t_1 + t_4 = t_2 = t_3 = D/3$$

This suggested that we should take the basic unit of time, u, to be $D/3$, since this quantity was repeated in every pulse. Equation (1) could then be written in the form:

$$(4) \quad \frac{D^2 / u^2}{T/u} = A'$$

or:

$$(5) \quad 3D/T = A'$$

Moffet[6] gives the value for the pulse period of C.P. 1919, $T = 1.337301092$ sec. If D were equal to .0355 sec., then A' would have the very interesting value of $1/4\pi$. In fact, the measured value of D is $.037 \pm .004$ seconds.

The number 4π is of course an important physical constant which would likely be recognized by any civilization sophisticated enough to build a receiver to detect modulated electromagnetic radiations. Although such an approach is arbitrary and contains several weaknesses, it does illustrate the type of message, type of decoding process and the type of result that might be involved in any search conducted by or for extraterrestrial intelligence. It also raises the question: At what level of precision should such transmissions of suspected basic numerical referents become worthy of serious attention?

CONCLUSIONS

Establishing communication requires being in the right place at the right time, a commonly accessible channel, overlap of previous experience, intent to communicate, common concepts of time, order, and interval, and some common technology. These coincidences suggest that establishing communications between alien species may not be easy and that many intelligences might exist in parallel without communications. Indeed there are ample examples of this on our own planet. These generalizations can be used to form a set of concepts about how an encoding key might be defined. With these in hand, the signals from pulsar C.P. 1919 were examined and it was found possible to identify a constant, 4π, embedded within the signal. The appearance of this constant here is undoubtedly a coincidence. In fact, by a sufficient number of arbitrarily chosen steps it should be possible to find 4π or some other basic quantity "buried" in all types of data. This is not the challenge. The task is to design criteria of economy, comprehensiveness, and precision governing decoding steps that will lead to clearcut decisions as to whether something "non-natural" is present in the data that has not been put there by the decoder.

With increasing discoveries of complex cosmic signals of various forms, the precepts of this paper lead us to recommend that methodologies for analyzing these signals be developed to determine whether signal structure and variations represent some form of communication.

REFERENCES

1. H. Freudenthal, *Lincos: Design of a Language for Cosmic Intercourse*, North-Holland, Amsterdam, 1960.
2. B. M. Oliver, "Interstellar Communication," from *Interstellar Com-*

munication, A. G. W. Cameron, editor, W. A. Benjamin, Inc., New York, 1963, and C. Sagan and I. S. Shklovskii, *Intelligent Life in the Universe,* Holden-Day, Inc., San Francisco, 1966.

3. M. H. Segall, D. T. Campbell, M. J. Hershovitz, *The influence of Culture on Visual Perception,* Bobbs-Merrill Press, 1966.

4. F. D. Drake, "Pulse Structure of the Pulsating Radio Source in Vulpecula," *Science,* April 26, 1968, p. 416.

5. A. G. Lyne, R. J. Ricket, "Measurements of the Pulse Shape and Spectrum of the Pulsating Radio Sources," *Nature,* April 27, 1968, p. 326.

6. A. T. Moffet, R. D. Ekers, "Detection of the Pulsed Radio Source CP 1919 at 13 cm Wavelength," *Nature,* April 20, 1968, p. 227.

6

F. J. DYSON

Search for Artificial
Stellar Sources
of Infrared Radiation

Dr. Freeman Dyson of the Princeton Institute for Advanced Study suggested in 1960 that an intelligent civilization, faced with the necessity of utilizing all of the resources available to it, might rearrange the mass of its planets into a spherical shell surrounding its sun. This would provide maximum surface area for raising food and living space. The inner surface of the shell would be illuminated everywhere; almost all of the power radiated from the star would be usable rather than being wasted on an endless trip in space. In the article which follows, Dr. Dyson argues that this kind of restructuring of a solar system is reasonable, and he proposes that we scan the heavens looking for point sources of infrared radiation which would leak through such a shell.

Cocconi and Morrison[1] have called attention to the importance and feasibility of listening for radio signals transmitted by extraterrestrial intelligent beings. They propose that listening aerials be directed toward nearby stars which might be accompanied by planets carrying such beings. Their proposal is now being implemented.[2]

The purpose of this report is to point out other possibilities which ought to be considered in planning any serious search for evidence of extraterrestrial intelligent beings. We start from the notion that the time scale for industrial and technical development of these beings is likely to be very short in comparison with the time scale of stellar evolution. It is therefore overwhelmingly probable that any such beings observed by us will have been in existence for millions of years, and will have already reached a technological level surpassing ours by many orders of magnitude. It is then a reasonable working hypothesis that their habitat will have been expanded to the limits set by Malthusian principles.

We have no direct knowledge of the material conditions which these beings would encounter in their search for lebensraum. We therefore consider what would be the likely course of events if these beings had originated in a solar system identical with ours. Taking our own solar system as the model, we shall reach at least a possible picture of what may be expected to happen elsewhere. I do not argue that this is what *will* happen in our system; I only say that this is what *may have* happened in other systems.

The material factors which ultimately limit the expansion of a technically advanced species are the supply of matter and the supply of energy. At present the material resources being exploited by the human species are roughly limited to the biosphere of the earth, a mass of the order of 5×10^{19} grams. Our present energy supply may be generously estimated at 10^{20} ergs per second. The quantities of matter and energy which might conceivably become accessible to us within the solar system are 2×10^{30} grams (the mass of Jupiter) and 4×10^{33} ergs per second (the total energy output of the sun).

The reader may well ask in what sense can anyone speak of the mass of Jupiter or the total radiation from the sun as being accessible to exploitation. The following argument is intended to show that an exploitation of this magnitude is not absurd. First of all, the time required for an expansion of population and industry by a factor of 10^{12} is quite short, say 3000 years if an average growth rate of 1 per cent per year is maintained. Second, the energy required to disassemble and rearrange a planet of the size of Jupiter is about 10^{44} ergs, equal to the energy radiated by the sun in 800 years. Third, the mass of Jupiter, if distributed in a spherical shell revolving around the sun at twice the Earth's distance from it, would have a thickness such that the mass is 200 grams per square centimeter of surface area (2 to 3 meters, depending on the density). A shell of this thickness could be made comfortably habitable, and could contain all the machinery required for exploiting the solar radiation falling onto it from the inside.

It is remarkable that the time scale of industrial expansion, the mass of Jupiter, the energy output of the sun, and the thickness of a habitable biosphere all have consistent orders of magnitude. It seems, then, a reasonable expectation that, barring accidents, Malthusian pressures will ultimately drive an intelligent species to adopt some such efficient exploitation of its available resources. One should expect that, within a few thousand years of its entering the stage of industrial development, any intelligent species should be found occupying an artificial biosphere which completely surrounds its parent star.

If the foregoing argument is accepted, then the search for extraterrestrial intelligent beings should not be confined to the neighborhood of visible stars. The most likely habitat for such beings would be a dark object, having a size comparable with the Earth's orbit, and a surface temperature of 200° to 300° K. Such a dark object would be radiating as copiously as the star which is hidden inside it, but the radiation would be in the far infrared, around 10 microns wavelength.

It happens that the Earth's atmosphere is transparent to radiation with wavelength in the range from 8 to 12 microns. It is therefore feasible to search for "infrared stars" in this range of wavelengths, using existing telescopes on the Earth's surface. Radiation in this range from Mars and Venus has not only been detected but has been spectroscopically analyzed in some detail.[3]

I propose, then, that a search for point sources of infrared radiation be attempted, either independently or in conjunction with the search for artificial radio emissions. A scan of the entire sky for objects down to the 5th or 6th magnitude would be desirable, but is probably beyond the capability of existing techniques of detection. If an undirected scan is impossible, it would be worthwhile as a preliminary measure to look for anomalously intense radiation in the 10-micron range associated with visible stars. Such radiation might be seen in the neighborhood of a visible star under either of two conditions. A race of intelligent beings might be unable to exploit fully the energy radiated by their star because of an insufficiency of accessible matter, or they might live in an artificial biosphere surrounding one star of a multiple system, in which one or more component stars are unsuitable for exploitation and would still be visible to us. It is impossible to guess the probability that either of these circumstances would arise for a particular race of extraterrestrial intelligent beings. But it is reasonable to begin the search for infrared radiation of artificial origin by looking in the direction of nearby visible stars, and especially in the direction of stars which are known to be binaries with invisible companions.

REFERENCES

1. G. Cocconi and P. Morrison, *Nature* 184, 844, 1959.
2. *Science* 131, 1303, Apr. 29, 1960.
3. W. M. Sinton and J. Strong, *Astrophys. J.* 131, 459, 470, 1960.

7

G. MURPHY

Psychology in
the Year 2000

Professor Gardner Murphy is a member of the Department of Psychology, George Washington University. The following piece, which deals with the future of psychology, appeared in the American Psychologist. It is included here because it tells of the prospective reorientation of the discipline. In a broad panoramic sweep it carries us one hundred years beyond Freud into a time when man will have the ability to scan himself internally, to control reactions and organs previously thought to be autonomic, to select drugs which can elicit experience of tremendous diversity, and to exist in new states of consciousness or contemplation. It raises the possibility that parapsychology may become "good" science and exist "in harmony with general psychological principles." In short, it tells of the time when man, through new understanding of the mind, will gain new perceptions and expectations about himself.

Our profound ambivalence about human futures, and our hopes and fears regarding the possibility of intelligent planning for the future, appears in a charming phrase of Sir George Thomson. Regarding the role of science in planning for new potentialities within the human germ cell, he says that the likelihood of genetic improvements is about like the probability of improving a statue by spraying it with machine gun bullets. Instantly, however, he catches himself up in the remark that with the electron microscope, the localization of individual genes is already very close. One dares not be overbold for fear the critics will laugh, while actually the science fiction and the casual predictions of scientists for the last hundred years or so have been much too modest—in fact, much too myopic—as to what actually can be achieved. The best guide here is a systematic and reasonable extrapolation from indentifiable trends and, at the same time, a cautious but systematic utilization of the principle of emergence in which new realities constantly come into being, not through the extrapolation of separate curves, but through specific interaction processes. Many of these new emergents are known in metallurgy, in embryology, and in the field of psychology. Some of them have to do with new perceptual and conceptual wholes as shown in countless studies of music and of painting; some of them have to do with dyadic or group patterns that come into existence when new relationships are achieved for the first time, as shown in the dynamic leadership patterns of Lewin, White, and Lippitt. In a symposium like the present one, an ultracautious note may indeed *sound* like science, but only like the plodding science of Sir Francis Bacon's *Novum Organum*, not the creative science that indeed has remade the world, and is remaking the world through the extravagant inventiveness of a Planck and an Einstein. In this spirit, I shall attempt some predictions that, I believe, are just as likely to prove shallow and banal as to prove ultimately extravagant and exotic.

The ten topics which I shall attempt to survey are extrapolations based upon (*a*) the current extraordinary development of *psychophysiology;* (*b*) together with such psychophysiology, the new possibilities of *internal scanning,* in the discovery of the inner human world; the renewed capacity to *observe, with full objectivity, a great deal that has long been regarded as hopelessly subjective;* (*c*) herewith, the direct *confrontation of the unconscious world* that merges into, and is isomorphic with, the world of physiology; (*d*) following these discoveries, the development of *voluntary control over the inner world,* such as scientists previously never dared to dream; (*e*) a new definition of a wide variety of nameless states, *psychological states for which there are no good names,* including feeling states, cognitive states, and volitional states, upon which human destiny almost literally may depend, with resulting understanding of those profound alterations in states of consciousness, well known to the East, regarding which Western man usually has expressed doubt or scorn; (*f*) together with these, the objective exploration of the vast sphere of *parapsychology,* at the edges of which science is nibbling, but so far has failed massively to invade; (*g*) a fresh *reconsideration of the relations of psychology to the biological sciences,* especially genetics; (*h*) a renewed *consideration of psychology in relation to the social sciences,* notably in the new science of social ecology, entailing cross-cultural collaboration of cross-cultural realities; (*i*) a note on the way in which changes in research *methods* alter all these basic concepts; (*j*) finally, a consideration, in all these terms, of the nature of the *human predicament* to which expanding science, which I am describing, may make a serious and indeed a crucial contribution.

First, then, as to psychophysiology. Partly as a result of new concepts of the wholeness, the integrity, of the living system, as voiced for example by Sir Charles Sherrington in the *Integrative Action of the Nervous System,* and partly as a result of the sheer power of the research tools that have been developed, psychophysiology has become a dramatically new science in recent decades. Problems of specialization and subspecialization of tissues, as within the mammalian cerebral cortex, have assumed astonishing forms with Penfield's discovery of specific memory localization, with various techniques for studying the electronic functional realities inside the individual nerve cell, with X-ray studies of lattices, and with fine localization of sensory and motor function through implanted electrodes. Both the cruder spot localizations, earlier used in the study of the aphasias, and also the extreme equipotentiality concepts, based largely on extirpation studies, have yielded to a dialectical reconsideration of both local and general aspects of functioning, and with an extraordinary directness of application to the world of immediate experience. Donald Hebb's brilliant breakthrough in the study of sensory deprivation has helped scientists to think of the amazing possibilities of sensory enrichment. One can no longer speak of sensory deprivation or sensory enrichment without thinking, in the manner of David Krech, about the biochemistry and physiology of the mammalian cortex, as profoundly affected by very early postnatal experience. One begins to see, quite literally, the likelihood, in the next few decades, of a thoroughgoing isomorphism of physiological process and psychological process right across the board. Biochemical and neurophysiological progress has been so astonishing in the last few years that psychologists may look quite confidently for a rapidly advancing series of discoveries related specifically to the different kinds of human experience, essentially the sensory, the imaginal, the conceptual, the affective, and indeed certain types of experience that have never been analyzed finely enough to name. Psychopharmacology, long considered to be limited to the specific effects of toxins, is rapidly taking on the form of a powerful organist having at his command banks upon banks of keys, and hundreds of stops, calling into existence an incredible gamut of new experiences.

INTERNAL SCANNING

Following from, or upon, this concurrent study of psychophysiology and biochemistry on the one hand, and the phenomenal world of immediate experience and function on the other hand, psychologists will be drawn, as in a vortex, into the rich field of the study of internal scanning. By this I mean, first, the process by which delicate messages from the striped musculature can be identified more accurately as our subjects carry out reflex or skilled movements. Like a tea taster or a wine sampler the subject, in several laboratories today, recognizes quickly the kinesthetic messages in different magnitude from different muscles. Specific muscular activities are experienced kinesthetically at the same time he sees on the panel the electronic evidence of what is occurring in specific muscle groups so that he learns to identify and name them. He is learning, in the same way, to recognize on the panel many other messages that come from organs that are under autonomic control. One may think of the studies by the U.S.S.R. scientists Bykov and Lisina relating to proprioceptive and interoceptive conditioning.

But the work will soon move further along. Giving the subject feedback on a panel that shows him what specific internal activities are going on, he can be taught to make more and more refined differentiation within the inner world. His searching, his sweeping, his scanning, and his identifying of the different components from the proprioceptive world, as identical or isomorphic with the same messages from the exteroceptive world on the panel or conveyed to him through tones, give him more and more information as to the rich system of internal messages that have previously been nearly a blur, so precise that he can begin to play the instrument himself. The ancient prejudice that exteroceptive information has a kind of place in the reality world, which is lacking for the other sensory functions, has begun to collapse. A rich variety of internal messages has exactly the same possibility of cross-checking, consensual validation, as has held for sight, hearing, and touch. It is hard to set any limits. Something is known about discriminability when working with teas and wines or even two-point thresholds on the finger tip, but these studies have never been pushed to their true physiological limits. Nor is it known how they are affected by a variety of parameters, anatomical distribution of receptors and afferent fibers, which in the past have never been sufficiently important to investigate; but today they are being seen in terms of individuality—an individuality based upon heredity, growth, and the learning process. A whole internal world is awaiting discovery.

CONFRONTATION OF THE UNCONSCIOUS WORLD

Third, this internal world, as Gregory Razran has pointed out, would include the entire world of the "observable unconscious," the world of psychologically meaningful, but hitherto not directly observable, processes discovered by Freud and his followers. More and more it appears to be the same world as that which anthropologists, playwrights, poets, and prophets have often enjoined without knowing, in any scientific sense, what they were doing.

But it is one thing to observe the separate components, of course, and another thing to study creatively how they can be put together into new and emergent wholes. Both Arnheim, in *Art and Visual Perception,* and Freud, in *The Interpretation of Dreams,* have applied some of the first informative steps regarding the synthesis, the creative reorganization, of a world that offers vast possibilities. Literally there are hundreds of experiences waiting patiently to be discovered through experimentation. It will not be just the clinicians and the "encounter" groups that will discover them; such discoveries will soon yield rich new harvests to general experimental psychology. I might remind you that while Chaucer, six hundred years ago, had only a few words for colors, there are today some thousands of color terms, mostly representing *new* colors that have evolved in the last century as a result of industrial chemistry—colors that do not appear in any rainbow, natural sunset, or natural color schema. There are not only the stock experiences that human beings have by virtue of their anatomical equipment and their physiological capacity as human beings, but thousands of newly created colors. There also are many new kinds of inner experiences, ranging from the effects of new goods, drugs, smogs, exercise, fatigue, strain, anxiety, and ecstasy—scores upon scores of new kinds and shades of inner experience. Of course, many of the new methods may involve risks, and many of them will come under some sort of social control. Whether it will be control by a wise and humane Federal agency, or by public opinion, no present reliable clues are extant.

Inner responses include those called affective and impulsive states, and the vast range of expressions of mood and temperament used in the aesthetic world and in the personal world generally. There are new worlds just waiting; and they will not have to wait very long. Experimental methods for the study of differentiation are developing; for example, experiments in the Soviet Union proved that two-point thresholds within the body, say from the gastric mucosa, can be measured. It is believable that as such differentiations are carried out by classical psychophysical methods, experimenters may first identify a very large range of internal messages and, second, may learn how to integrate them in thousands of new ways.

VOLUNTARY CONTROL

Fourth, insofar as these new messages can be differentiated, tagged, and named, they apparently can be brought under voluntary control. A wide array of new possibilities exists, for example, in Hefferline's study of rapid acquisition of operant control over slight movements that are effective in cutting out a disagreeable hum spoiling music at the time. That is, individuals who could differentiate at all could also learn, even though unwittingly, to bring in or shut out particular messages. Other laboratories are now continuing what Hefferline started. It appears to be a very refined, delicate, and far-below-threshold type of activity that can bring in an astonishing range of experimentally prepared visual and auditory material. Soviet work on voluntary control of cardiovascular processes appears to concur with what Robert Malmo has reported in Montreal. There are studies of bladder and of capillary control, using panel feedback techniques, strongly suggesting that the autonomically controlled organs are capable of being brought rapidly into the same sphere of voluntary control as that which obtains for the striped muscle responses. Within the next decade or two certainly a very significant control of cardiovascular and gastrointestinal responses may be anticipated, not only with immediate clinical values in bringing in or shutting out various classes of bodily information, but with the deeper scientific value of giving a much wider view of what the human potentialities for such inner experience and such inner control may be. Wenger and Bagchi studied adepts in yoga in various ashrams in India, while Anand and his collaborators pushed their studies further. The keen interest of Indian investigators in putting to experimental tests the classical yoga sutras of Patanjali means not only cross-national research collaboration but, what is more important, the serious awakening of Western psychologists to the fact that experiences treasured and cultivated on the other side of the globe may be as worthy of investigation as those encountered in Detroit, Cambridge, or Topeka.

Last, but by no means least, the process of directly observing one's own electroencephalogram, notably one's own alpha, was developed by Joe Kamiya at Langley Porter and independently by Barbara Brown at the Sepulveda Veterans Administration Hospital. With Kamiya, a 400-cycle tone is activated by the individual's own alpha rhythm, so the subject given the task of increasing the amount of alpha he is exhibiting can rapidly learn, through the feedback that this tone gives him, to bring this under his control. Soon he is turning on or turning off his own alpha. Apparently alpha is not the only rhythm that he can control. There are staggering possibilities both for the understanding of the nature of central nervous system control by the organized central nervous system itself in the form that is called voluntary, but likewise a vast area of further implications for the understanding of the isomorphic relation between a variety of subjective states that accompany the alpha and the exteroceptive patterns that are seen when observing the visual tracing or hearing an appropriate tone. While the clinical applications are important, it is this larger vision of learning to control the brain rhythms themselves that is likely to mean most to the scientist oriented to the year 2000.

NAMELESS STATES

Fifth, while neither Kamiya, nor anyone else so far as I know, has published the implications that these new methods have for the study of whole new areas of experience only dimly describable today, it is highly probable that before the year 2000 there will be both identification of many kinds of phenomenological states that are anchored upon particular types of EEGs, and the invention of appropriate *names,* appropriate language to describe the newly identified and newly integrated components. I am thinking particularly of cognitive states, conceptualizing states, creative states that may, while retaining all their charm and all their majesty, become far more describable, controllable, and achievable.

PARAPSYCHOLOGY

Sixth, it is characteristic science at any given period to cultivate the belief that it has a rather well-integrated system into which new observations can fit. While it is at many points open-ended, with really fuzzy edges, there would be chaos indeed if scientists relinquished their passion for a unified field of science. Suppose science was an archipelago of little, spotty, factual details, with no possibility of an implied closed system, an ocean bed unifying all the little islands that appear at the surface level. There is very good psychological reason why science, as it grows, takes on the conservative, the resistive character that is apparent. Under these conditions it is hardly surprising that there is some restlessness or even resistance when talking about the discovery of kinds of experience about which nothing has been known. Of course, there are many good reasons, in polite society, why people do not know too much about their insides. These have to do with delicate and complex systems of human expression, some related very broadly to love, some related very broadly to destructiveness, but a great many others that almost every human individual encounters, but does not really want at this time to communicate on a massive basis. I do not anticipate very much actual interference with science on this count, but I do think one must be honest in admitting that this quest of the inside will entail not only triumphs but occasional acrimonious encounters.

While saying this I must add that the resistance toward types of human communication, which presently are not understood, had shown the same attributes. One can understand very clearly the natural fear of scientists that their whole tough labor would be disturbed if they should admit perceptual, memoric, affective, or volitional processes that now are not explainable in terms of the basic biochemical and biophysical realities of human conduct. Even the thought elements that the Würzburg School brought into Wundt's psychological system led to much hostility. Today more serious difficulties are being dealt with as the study of *parapsychology* moves into more systematic experimental form. Most of the data, when closely observed, are like the perceptual and affective data already known, but appear to occur under conditions in which the time and space parameters are unfamiliar. For example, in several recent studies, the telepathic phenomena occur when sender and receiver are separated by very long distances; and while the data can be described psychologically without any mystery, a physical difficulty is encountered because how to conceptualize energies that could carry over these long distances is not known. In other words, the difficulty is at the level of physics, not at the level of psychology. Psychologists may be a little bewildered when they encounter modern physicists who take these phenomena in stride; in fact, take them very much more seriously than psychologists do, saying, as physicists, that they are no longer bound by the types of Newtonian energy distribution, inverse square laws, etc., with which scientists used to regard themselves as tightly bound. In the same way, new physical conceptions regarding the nature of time seem to remove a large part of the trouble that appears in precognition experiments, in which a randomly determined target order of stimulus materials can be foreseen by certain subjects. I think that with the computer methods that are now coming into use, and with the progressive rigidity in experimental controls, psychologists probably will witness a period of slow, but definite, erosion of the blandly exclusive attitude that has offered itself as the only appropriate scientific attitude in this field. The data from parapsychology will be almost certainly in harmony with general psychological principles, and will be assimilated rather easily within the systematic framework of psychology as a science when once the imagined appropriateness of Newtonian physics is put aside, and modern physics replaces it.

PSYCHOLOGY AND BIOLOGY

As I turn to genetics, I would venture to predict a period of massive reorientation of psychology to the biological roots of which it used to boast. The very substance of growth, of motivation, of the learning process, and indeed of most of the basic realities with which the modern evolutionary psychology will have to cope, are provided by the DNA-RNA system; the elements of field physics as they are known in the embryology of Spemann and Weiss; the intricacies of polygenic determination of structure and function; and the broad recognition that individuality in tissue systems, as described by Roger Williams, rewrites the psychology of individual differences in astonishing terms. These genetic terms, of course, will be held by some to be fatalistic, as indicating the genetically given limitations upon all human endeavor. But in two respects these discoveries will be most encouraging: (a) It will be realized that individuality always applies to the growth *potential*, which can be utterly different when a new environmental situation is supplied. An example is the discovery of the Mendelian basis of the phenylpyruvic type of mental defect that has nevertheless yielded, to a large degree, to a carefully prepared diet. In other words, that which was genetically determined was controllable. Through respect for the genetics of human individuality, how to become better environmentalists will be understood. (b) As Sir George Thomson's statement, quoted earlier, implied, scientific insight is moving rapidly to a point such that the electron microscope can greatly aid in studies of the internal organization of individual cells. This, together with some control of mutations and a great deal of control of selective breeding and the application of the principles of population genetics, makes it likely that within a few generations, to a considerable degree, some of the most abhorrent threats to human development may be eliminated. In anticipating the year 2100 or 2500, biologists could talk quite rationally about not only the prevention of deterioration, but plans for the actual long-range improvement of genetic potentials.

PSYCHOLOGY AND SOCIAL SCIENCE

But the biological sciences do not have the whole exigent message. There is equal need for big gains in the social sciences, especially in the development of a social ecology. Ecology has been the most neglected aspect, I think, of the entire behavior field. The experimental psychologist may control, say, a $10 \times 10 \times 10$ foot area, and, with enormous and devoted attention to detail, think of everything that is in that space at a given time. Organisms, however, have life histories in segments of space time about which a fair amount is known if they are hatched or born in the laboratory. But if not, the higher they are in the phylogenic tree, the more likely they are to bring more from their past into the laboratory. Mark May used to say that the American sophomore, from whom are derived findings from humanity at large, was expected to "park his culture outside." Only the regions of time and space that are involved in the experiment are observed, ignoring the whole vast area from which the individual organism comes.

The needed studies of ecological organization are vastly more complex than anybody has imagined so far. The maps that Roger Barker has drawn of a Kansas town and the lists of situational pressures that Saul Sells has devised as a preparation for space travel will be only a tiny sampling of the vast conception of past and present environmental totalities that Egon Brunswik asked scientists to imagine. It will be a genetics that is oriented to a systematic and scientific science of ecology that will really give new field clues to human behavior. By field clues I hope to suggest the modalities of interaction between the edge of the organism and the edge of the environment, such that a complete and real fusion is created. I mean the kind of thing that is involved in interaction between the visual centers in the brain, the retina, the external light source, the laboratory conditions, personalities of the experimenters, the laboratory tradition, and laboratory culture, all of which must be considered when a person sees an inkblot or a social scene enacted before him. There must be whole organisms and whole environments to be studied for the sake of the modalities of reciprocity that develop between them. Psychologists began to learn from Lewin, as earlier they began to learn from Clerk-Maxwell, how to think in field terms; but they really have not done much of the sort on a scale demanded by present knowledge. The subspecialization has driven them more and more from organs to tissues, from tissues to cells, from cells to molecules, from molecules to atoms, from atoms to microparticles. All this specialization is, of course, absolutely necessary. The job of seeing psychological function, however, in combined biological and cultural terms is mostly a promissory note with as yet very little backing.

Because of its rarity, I shall mention the example of audiogenic seizures in mice, which Benson Ginzburg showed to have a not too complex Mendelian basis. But some of the mice that were expected to have convulsions and die had no convulsions, or had convulsions but did not die. He then attacked the problem from the pharmacological viewpoint and, in terms of biochemistry, found a way to buffer the lethal effects of the genes. Allow me a free analogy in the field of human ecology: What will happen when one finds a human environment of space-time-sensory enrichment, maternal warmth, generous and skillful experimental reinforcement that will allow a poorly endowed, frightened, aggressive ghetto child to develop into full humanness? This is exactly the type of experiment now being launched at several outposts of research on disadvantaged children. Before long thought in terms of biology versus the social sciences will cease; an ecological science will be developed so rich and so concrete that it will articulate closely with the new biology of individual growth.

And if psychologists mean quite seriously that man, as man, is richly intertwined with his ecology, it follows that the psychology of the next two decades will depend enormously upon the discovery of new forms of cross-cultural, cross-national communication. Indeed, it follows that unless there is very broad cross-national communication and action, there will be no human race to investigate. It will not do for American psychology, now having about 92 per cent of the world's psychological personnel and about 92 per cent of its published communications, to undertake a bland and supposedly disinterested study of the rest of the world in order that the wise and productive science, which they represent, can convey appropriate knowledge to those struggling along in less enlightened paths of endeavor. The study of the human predicament can come from a human race familiar with the method of science, but a human race speaking many tongues, regarding many values, and holding different convictions about the meaning of life sooner or later will have to consult all that is human. There are a few living today who will still be alive in the year 2000, if there is a year 2000; and I hope they will still be battling the problem of developing a sufficiently coherent, human enough point of view to speak for all kinds of human beings. This will mean that the genetic and ecological progress that I am describing will have actually helped toward a psychology that is common human, that entails not only a study of all human beings, but a study by trained and devoted individuals within all human groups. Following the American habit of delivering "State of the Union" messages, the Secretary-General of the United Nations has been asked to report on the "state of the human race." I personally do not understand why governments and indeed professional psychologists, as well, are almost wholly ignoring the challenge to study directly the possibilities of achieving an international and intercultural plan for world order. Aiming at this goal, it is conceivable that there will be worldwide human modalities of investigation like those already existing in astronomy and in medicine, but oriented to the behavioral sciences. And it is even possible that they will be oriented not only to the behaviors as such, but toward the deep inner humanness that I have tried to describe as an object of study. This, in relation to the dyadic and group problems of the behavior sciences, may give both insight and control over the more destructive tendencies, and may utilize the common human aspiration to live not only more safely and a little more comfortably, but also a little more creatively and a great deal more humanly.

THE ROLE OF METHOD

You have noted that new discoveries in the field of psychology, and, I believe, in all scientific fields, are largely the children of new *methods*. Consider what the compound microscope did to histology, what X rays did for diagnostic procedure, and what the puzzle box, the maze, the Skinner box have done in the development and documentation of seminal scientific theories. I am raising these issues not simply to welcome the computer to our side, as a new brother, but to ask one final question. Psychologists can, as A. H. Maslow has pointed out, strip down the study of man to those methods common to the other sciences that do not deal with man; they can assume that the human sciences can best do their job by leaving humanness out. There is, however, another possibility. They might conceivably find that science can become big enough to develop fully human methods oriented to the complete panoply of human problems, that empathy, "tlc," rich dyadic methods of communication between subjects and experimenters, through patience, discipline, and imagination, might give them in the year 2000 a science more competent to deal with all the discoverable aspects of human nature.

But a still more basic problem of method relates to the way in which they try to hook together the data from laboratory, from clinic, from field observation, from home, from neighborhood, and from observation of human gatherings in schools, churches, juries, parliamentary bodies. On the one hand, they have neglected the use of laboratories, and today they are beginning to discover a more suitable laboratory approach to a wide variety of spontaneous human situations. They are discovering that inventive experimentalists can do even better work in free human situations than they can in the classical, highly planned, settings. But now I am referring mainly to the manner in which the experimental method does its work. Long ago, psychologists established for themselves the impossible task of creating a psychology through intensive observation of those phenomena that occur under controlled laboratory conditions, and then systematizing a psychology based solely on such findings. They tried to set up physics and chemistry, sometimes the biological sciences of genetics, embryology, and physiology, as models. Belatedly they have discovered that beautiful scientific structures such as that of modern geology, with only slight use of experimental method, can be developed through the integration of many types of observations, short-term and long-term, outdoors and indoors, pinpointed, or extravagantly blown up to cosmic proportions. The geolgist uses experimental methods, but he uses them in the total context of his work. It is mother earth, not her fingernails, that interests him. Psychology, which attempted to pinpoint its existence in the nineteenth-century terms of Weber and Fechner, is now beginning a great awakening, a sort of Rip Van Winkle awakening; for we are discovering, and will discover more fully in the next few decades, the vast dimensions in which a mature psychology can be conceived. It will make even more use of experimental method than it does at present. But the experiments will be suggested, and the techniques controlled, rather largely by the broad perception of the nature of the human animal in his whole ecological setting. The observational systems that will develop cannot be categorized by any one word that is now known. The word *experimental* is a fine word, but it will have to be replaced by something much more systematic. Even the developmental approach will mean something quite new when conceived in the kind of general systems terms, the kind of life science terms, that I am trying to suggest. Mathematical models certainly will both benefit and be benefited by the transitions that I am suggesting; and, of course, the engineering skills, already so important in psychophysiology, will become even more important.

I think psychologists will have to admit that many of this era will be unable to see the promised land that begins to be sketched out. Psychologists who will be extant in the year 2000 will have to be smarter than the psychologists today, as well as enormously better trained—I might add, enormously more *broadly* trained—than the subspecialized people turned out today. The blade of the modern mind is sharpened until it breaks, and we damn the blade instead of asking the metallurgist to develop tools from which sharp weapons can be prepared that, while still unscathed, can cut through the hard inscrutable rock of man's basic resistance to discovering his own nature.

THE HUMAN PREDICAMENT

The year 2000 can come, and the twenty-first century can offer less terror and more joy, but only if psychologists have learned both *how to look inside* and *how to look outside;* how to recognize the reciprocities of inner and outer, through methods that are as far ranging and as deeply human as is the human stuff that is being studied.

8

T. BACON *and*

R. KIRKPATRICK

Do Plants
Feel Emotions?

Plant life differs from animal life in profound and basic ways. Animals feel emotions—fear, anger, pain—and even the simpler forms such as flat worms can be stimulated by electrical shock. The concept that the ability to feel emotions constitutes a basic difference between plants and animals has been challenged by Cleve Backster, a former interrogation specialist for the CIA who now operates his own school for the training of law enforcement officers in the use of the polygraph or "lie detector." The polygraph functions by measuring small physiological changes in the subject including changes in the electrical resistance of the skin. In the experiments described here, Mr. Backster measured the electrical resistance of certain plants with his polygraph apparatus and detected what appear to be emotional responses in the plants, responses to injury and the threat of injury, responses that occur even if the injury is only thought about by the experimenter.

The article is by Thorn Bacon, writer for the conservation magazine National Wildlife. *It reports on an interview between Mr. Bacon and Mr. Backster. The editors of* National Wildlife *were understandably skeptical of the report and dispatched their own staff to Mr. Backster's laboratory. Mr. Kirkpatrick records their findings at the conclusion of the article.*

Suppose you were to be told that the philodendron plant resting on the window sill above your kitchen sink screams silently when you break a breakfast egg in the frying pan, or that the potted dracaena on the sun porch grows apprehensive whenever your dog goes by?

Finally, would you dare believe that when you accidentally cut your finger the dying cells in the drying blood transmit signals to the philodendron, the dracaena and the parsley in your refrigerator?

Provocative questions? Indeed, yes, but ones which are being seriously, soberly and quietly investigated by scientists at several major American universities as a result of some bizarre findings by the Backster Research Foundation of New York City.

The object: To discover if there is an unknown communication link between the cells of plants and animals through which distress signals are transmitted that broadcast threats against any member of the living community!

These staggering implications were reported in an abstract published on September 7, 1967, by Cleve Backster, a former interrogation specialist with the Central Intelligence Agency, who operates a New York school for training law enforcement officers in the techniques of using the polygraph—commonly known as the lie detector.

Backster was one of a four-man panel of experts called to testify before the 1964 Congressional Hearings on the Use of Polygraphs by the Federal Government. Following duty with the CIA as an interrogation specialist, he became director of the Leonarde Keeler Polygraph Institute of Chicago. Since 1949, he has acted as a consultant to almost every government agency which makes use of the polygraph. He introduced the Backster Zone Comparison polygraph procedure, which is the technique standard at the U. S. Army Polygraph School.

Changed his life. Teaching polygraph, however, became a secondary interest to Backster on a February morning in 1966 when he made the discovery which changed his life.

These are the words he used to describe what happened in his laboratory that morning:

"Immediately following the watering of an office plant, I wondered if it would be possible to measure the rate at which water rose in a plant from the root area into the leaf. I chose the psychogalvanic reflex (PGR) index as a possible means of measuring the rate of moisture ascent. The pair of PGR electrodes could be attached to a leaf of the plant. Hopefully, by using the Wheatstone bridge circuitry involved, I could measure the increase in the plant leaf's moisture content onto the polygraph tape.

"Deciding to pursue the idea, I placed a psychogalvanic reflex electrode on each side of the same leaf of the nearby *Dracaena Massangeana* plant with a rubber band. The plant leaf was successfully balanced into the PGR circuitry, its electrical resistance falling within the resistance limit of the instrumentation.

"Contrary to my expectation, from the outset the plant leaf tracing exhibited a downward trend. Then, after about one minute of chart time, the tracing exhibited a contour similar to a PGR reaction pattern typically demonstrated by a human subject experiencing an emotional stimulation of short duration. Even though its tracing had failed to reflect the effect of the watering, the plant leaf did offer itself as a possibly unique source of data.

"As I watched the PGR tracing continue, I wondered if there could be a similarity between the tracing from the plant and a PGR tracing from a human. I decided to try to apply some equivalent to the threat-to-well-being principle, a well-established

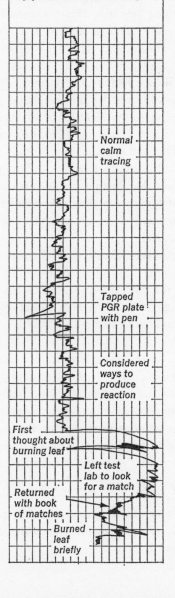

Further tracing from Backster's experiment of February 2, 1966, showing his first deliberate stimulation from a test plant. Backster regards it as significant that his intent to harm the plant produced a stronger reaction (anxiety?) than the actual burning.

Normal calm tracing

Tapped PGR plate with pen

Considered ways to produce reaction

First thought about burning leaf

Left test lab to look for a match

Returned with book of matches

Burned leaf briefly

method of triggering emotionality in humans. I first tried to arouse the plant by immersing a plant leaf in a cup of hot coffee. But there was no measurable reaction.

"After a nine minute interim, I decided to obtain a match and burn the plant leaf being tested. At the instant of this decision, at thirteen minutes, fifty-five seconds of chart time, here was a dramatic change in the PGR tracing pattern in the form of an abrupt and prolonged upward sweep of the recording pen. I had not moved or touched the plant, so the timing of the PGR pen activity suggested to me that the tracing might have been triggered by the mere thought of the harm I intended to inflict upon the plant. This occurrence, if repeatable, would tend to indicate the possible existence of some undefined perception in the plant."

Backster began to explore how the suffering of other species affected his plants. He bought some brine shrimp, ordinarily used as live food for tropical fish, and killed them by dumping them into boiling water. As he saw the polygraph recording needle leap frantically, he was awed by a startling and apparently new concept: "Could it be that when cell life dies, it broadcasts a signal to other living cells?" If this was so, he would have to completely automate his experiments, removing all human elements which might consciously or unconsciously contaminate the results.

Space-age lab. In the three years since, Backster has spent many thousands of dollars in transforming his offices into a space-age assembly of mechanized shrimp-dump dishes, a sophisticated electronic randomizer, and programmer circuitry and multiple PGR monitoring devices. But the results continue to point to a capability for perception in all living cells—a perception that Backster calls "primary." I asked him for more details:

Q. What do you mean by primary?

A. I mean primary in the sense that this perception applies to all cells that we have monitored, without regard to their assigned biological function.

Q. What types of cells have you tested?

A. We have found this same phenomenon in the amoeba, the paramecium, and other single-cell organisms, in fact, in every kind of cell we have tested: fresh fruits and vegetables, mold cultures, yeasts, scrapings from the roof of the mouth of a human, blood samples, even spermatozoa.

Q. Do you mean that all of these cells have a sensing capacity?

A. It seems so. Incidentally, we have tried unsuccessfully to block whatever signal is being received by using a Faraday screen, screen cage, and even lead-lined containers. Still the communication continues. It seems that the signal may not even fall within our electrodynamic spectrum. If not, this would certainly have profound implications.

Q. What kind of a signal is it?

A. I can answer your question better by telling you what we think the signal is *not*. We know it is not within the different known frequencies, AM, FM, or any form of signal which we can shield by ordinary means. Distance seems to impose no limitation. For example, we are conducting research that would tend to indicate that this signal can traverse hundreds of miles.

Q. Are plants attuned to stress?

A. Perhaps. I used to have a Doberman Pinscher in my office. He slept in the back room where I had an electric timer hooked to a loud pulsating alarm, which was located directly above his bed. Actuation of the timing mechanism was accompanied by a barely audible click which preceded the alarm by approximately five seconds. The dog would invariably hear the clock, and would leave the room before the bell, which he disliked intensely, started to ring. Although in a different room, with the plants, I knew exactly when the dog was leaving his room, even though I could not hear the click, because the plants acknowledged his movements by showing reaction coincidental to the click, reflecting the Doberman's anxiety.

Q. In the final analysis, aren't you saying that we must reassess our definitions of sensory perception and intelligence?

A. Who can say at this pont? There are certainly implications here that could have profound effects on those concepts. Our observations show that the signal leaps across distances, as I said before. I have been as far away as New Jersey—about fifteen miles from Manhattan—and have merely thought about returning to my office, only to learn when I returned that at the precise moment I had had the thought—checked against a stop watch—there was a coincidental reaction by the plants to the thought of coming back. Relief? Welcome? We aren't sure, but evidence indicates something like relief. It isn't fear.

Do plants have emotions? The trend of Backster's research results does indeed embrace profound implications. Do plants have emotions? Do they make strange signals of awareness beyond our own abilities to comprehend? It seems so. Personally, I cannot imagine a world so dull, so satiated, that it should reject out of hand arresting new ideas which may be as old as the first amino acid in the chain of life on our earth. Inexplicable has never meant miraculous. Nor does it necessarily mean spiritual. In this case, it may simply prove to mean another extension of our natural laws.

Let me leave you to ponder a question Backster asked me. Many hunters have observed that game animals somehow sense the exact moment of the opening of the hunting season. We can perhaps ascribe this to the noise of the first gunshots. But how can we explain the similar observation of game's apparent awareness of the exact moment of the season's close? Cleve Backster may be approaching the answer to that question, and a lot of others.

The editors of *National Wildlife* were as doubtful as you may be after reading Thorn Bacon's account of "Backster's Phenomenon," so we visited and photographed him in his offices, just off Times Square in New York City.

Typical plant reaction to a carefully randomized brine shrimp death, made on the automatic polygraph with no human in the laboratory.

Normal calm tracing

Mechanism actuates automatically

Shrimp dropped and killed.

Gradual return to normal calm

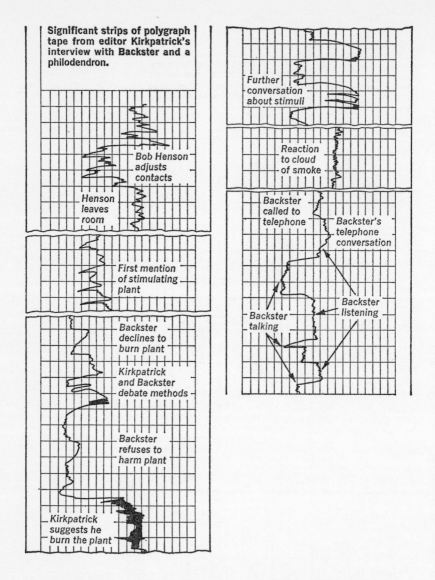

Significant strips of polygraph tape from editor Kirkpatrick's interview with Backster and a philodendron.

Bob Henson adjusts contacts

Henson leaves room

First mention of stimulating plant

Backster declines to burn plant

Kirkpatrick and Backster debate methods

Backster refuses to harm plant

Kirkpatrick suggests he burn the plant

Further conversation about stimuli

Reaction to cloud of smoke

Backster called to telephone

Backster's telephone conversation

Backster listening

Backster talking

We found a quiet, polite, serious, and successful student of the psychology of interrogation, working almost full time on the exploration of his discovery in an office cluttered with extremely sophisticated electronic gear and decorated with thumbtacked records of plant—and other cell life—reactions.

He showed us the original tape from his first discovery of the phenomenon and yard after yard of tapes from succeeding experiments. One thing impressed us immediately: First, Cleve Backster is not some kind of a nut. He really knows his business and is pursuing his investigations with great care to avoid any chance of criticism from the doubting scientific community, though he admits that seems inevitable.

As we talked, Backster set up his specially modified polygraph with a fairly ordinary philodendron leaf clamped in position for reading the psychogalvanic reflex index. He mentioned that he no longer handles his plants with anything but great care, since they seem to be attached to him as their owner and caretaker. When a plant must be handled or stimulated to produce a reaction, that is done by his assistant, Bob Henson, who "plays the heavy."

As we sat chatting, the pen traced a graph of normal repose for the plant, until Bob walked in the room. The graph turned suddenly to one of agitation and bobbed markedly until he left. Then it calmed down again to a normal tracing.

Later, we talked about ways to stimulate the plant for a photograph, and Backster explained that he preferred not to "hurt" the plant. I remarked that perhaps I could do it, and reached for a match, watching in astonishment as the plant produced a violently agitated reaction even as I began to speak.

Still later, the plant's readings became calmer and calmer, and Backster explained that after an extended time, they seemed to become accustomed to stimuli and their reactions became less marked. At that point I blew a cloud of cigarette smoke over the plant without warning, and it produced a jagged little graph that Backster didn't try to interpret but which I proclaimed to be a reaction of annoyance.

While George Harrison was shooting a photograph of the plant attached to the apparatus, Backster suddenly asked him if anything was wrong; the plant was showing something like a sympathetic reaction to consternation, but was not being stimulated in any way. George admitted that he had just discovered that one lens was not working properly and had been worrying about the photographs he had already made.

Altogether, we ran the machine on that plant for two hours, and produced a dozen very interesting reactions, some of which Backster recognized (though he is very reluctant to try to interpret them in human terms) and some others that made no particular sense at all, like the up-and-down reading yielded from a telephone conversation Backster held in a neighboring office. The plant reacted differently to the periods of Backster's talking and listening for some reason. But it did react.

So the reactions continue, and Cleve Backster's work continues, as he attempts to analyze the nature of the plants' graphs. Some of the possible applications of the phenomenon in medical diagnosis, criminal investigation, and other fields are so fantastic that he asked me not to repeat them here. His first serious paper on the phenomenon, titled "Evidence of a Primary Perception in Plant Life," is scheduled for publication in the *International Journal of Parapsychology* in January 1969. He awaits the reaction of the scientific community.

9

H. SCHMIDT

Anomalous Prediction
of Quantum Processes
by Some Human Subjects

This next piece is about ESP or more precisely, precognition, the ability to predict coming events through some intuitive sense. The experiments of Dr. J. B. Rhine and others in this field are fairly well known. For the most part these experiments have involved guessing which card would be turned over next, or which numbers would appear on the face of a pair of dice about to be rolled. These experiments have been criticized on the basis of possible misrecording by the experimenters, erroneous mathematical analysis of the data, or improper equipment (which might give the data unacceptable biases or provide the subjects with unwarranted clues).

Dr. Helmut Schmidt has built an apparatus which avoids these pitfalls and finds statistically significant evidence for precognition.

Imagine a subject seated in front of a small metal box. He can push one of four buttons. A small colored light is associated with each button. Typically, the subject selects the button in front of the light which he thinks will be energized next; he pushes it and then one of the lamps lights. Counters inside of the mechanism automatically record both the selection and the lamp which actually lights. Circuit is arranged to assure that each lamp will light as often as the others and that the pattern of lighting is completely random. In other words, in 10,000 trials each lamp can be expected to light 2500 times. That the circuit really produces these random results has been checked many times with a computer.

Most people obtain random scores from the box. Some people, however, consistently perform much better than chance. Somehow they manage to push the button in front of the light which actually lights more often than one ought to expect. The probability that the scores were chance alone is less than one in 500 million in one series of the test; for another, one in 10 billion.

Dr. Schmidt is a physicist who received his Ph.D. in 1954 at Cologne, Germany. He held a two-year research fellowship at Berkeley and taught physics at universities in the United States, Germany, and Canada. He built the device described in his article while he was a senior research physicist at the Boeing Company in Seattle. He is currently with the Institute for Parapsychology at Durham, North Carolina.

The research reported in this article was submitted by Dr. Schmidt in the journal Physical Review. *He has told me that they declined publication with the comment "The subject matter is not appropriate for a physics journal." Dr. Schmidt also said that* Science *rejected the piece despite a very favorable comment from their referee, giving as their reason: "After careful consideration we decided not to publish the paper." The British journal* New Scientist *recently contacted him and the research has been reported there in somewhat shortened but complete form.*

It is easy to build a device which generates the numbers 1, 2, 3, 4 such that in good approximation:

a) Each number appears with the same probability.

b) There is no correlation between generated numbers.

c) A quantum process determines which number is generated.

Such a device is described in detail later in this paper. The numbers obtained by triggering the system repeatedly then form a sequence of effectively random numbers. Experimental tests verifying this randomness have been performed and are also discussed later.

According to basic axioms of quantum theory, it should be impossible to predict the number to be generated upon next triggering this device with an accuracy of more than one fourth. In particular, if any person tries to predict the next number repeatedly, then the number of hits (correct predictions) should be, within the satistically expected fluctuations, approximately equal to one fourth of the number of trials.

In order to test this hypothesis experimentally, a large number of people was asked to predict a long series of generated random numbers. The person under study was seated in front of a panel with four push buttons and four corresponding colored lamps. The person tried to predict which of the lamps would light next, and registered the prediction by pressing the corresponding button. This pressing of a button triggered the generation of a random number and shortly afterward the number generated was displayed by the lighting of one lamp. (The objective of the person was to press the button next to the lamp which would light next.)

Particular efforts were made to keep the subjects happy during the experiment, slightly challenged, and confident in successful predicting. The experimental arrangement favored this since (a) the equipment was easily transportable and the subjects could work wherever they wanted, (b) the subjects could work at any speed they wanted, (c) stimulation was given by displaying the actually generated random numbers on brightly colored lamps, and (d) the automatic recording left the experimenter free from distracting routine work.

For most persons tested the number of hits was reasonably close to one fourth the number of trials, in agreement with the quantum-mechanical hypothesis concerning the unpredictability of quantum jumps.

A few people studied in these preliminary tests, however, fairly consistently seemed to obtain a slightly above-average number of hits. Some of these persons were selected for the first main experiment and several months later for the second main experiment.

In these two main experiments the numbers of hits obtained lie, on the average, by only 4.4 per cent and 8 per cent respectively above their expectation value. Due to the large number of trials made, however, these above-average scores are highly significant statistically and cannot be ascribed to statistical chance fluctuations.

The random number generator (RNG), the central part of the present equipment, is contained in a metal box ($9 \times 11 \times 3$ inches) which shows four lamps on top, four corresponding push buttons and mechanical counters.

The RNG was designed to preclude fraud by the subject and to eliminate recording errors by the experimenter. In particular, simultaneous pressing of several buttons or extremely fast pressing of many buttons in succession does not impair proper operation of the machine. If one of the mechanical push buttons is pressed, a corresponding electronic switch (flip-flop) is flipped, and within less than 10^{-6} sec. the other buttons are electronically blocked until the machine has, after approximately ½ second, completed the cycle described above, and all the buttons have been released. Furthermore, if it should ever happen that two (or more) buttons are pressed simultaneously with an accuracy such that two (or more) of the electronic switches flip, then the mechanical counters become blocked and this event is not registered.

The mechanical reset counters for the numbers of hits and trials are located on the front panel for the convenience of the subject and the experimenter. (Usually these counters were reset after one hundred trials and the results were written down by the experimenter.) The equipment also includes two non-reset counters. By reading these counters at the beginning and end of a series of trials and by comparing the result with the score obtained from the reset counter readings, errors in recording or adding of the results can be eliminated. Furthermore, the RNG was connected to a paper tape puncher which recorded in detail the buttons pressed and the random numbers generated. With this arrangement one more independent record of the numbers of hits and trials was obtained, and this detailed record is still available for any further analysis one might want to make.

For the interpretation of the experiments it is important to know whether the series of numbers produced by the RNG is sufficiently random so that this series does not have any pattern which the subject might detect and utilize for making correct predictions.

The randomness should be guaranteed theoretically as a result of the use of digital electronics in combination with a quantum device, provided no gross malfunction of the electronics occurred. Even though the electronic performance has been checked repeatedly, explicit randomness tests of the generated numbers seemed desirable and were performed.

Therefore, before, between, and after the tests of the main experiments, the RNG was used to generate a large sample of numbers which was recorded on paper tape for later evaluation. The generation of the numbers was triggered by a time clock which automatically pressed (at the rate of 1–2 per sec.) the button corresponding to the lamp number four. Approximately 4.7×10^6 numbers were recorded, on about one hundred days within an eighteen-month period.

A computer evaluation of these numbers did not suggest any, even temporary, deviation from the theoretically expected randomness.

Soon after the RNG was built, a physicist, Dr. D.W., demonstrated that he could "beat" the device. He made N=7600

trials in predicting the number to be generated next and obtained 2065 hits, which lies 4.37 standard deviations above the expectation value $N/4$. The probability for obtaining in 7600 trials such a high or a higher number of hits is 1:150,000.

After this a new RNG, having some additional safety features, was built and electronically and statistically checked. Among a large number (perhaps one hundred) of people tested with this device only a few seemed to be outstandingly successful in predicting random numbers. These preliminary tests suggested that successful prediction requires carefully selected subjects and favorable psychological conditions, i.e., a good momentary disposition of the subject and an encouraging attitude of the experimenter. The following main experiments, however, were not concerned with psychological details but only with the question of *existence* of the effect of anomalous prediction.

Three persons performed the first main experiment. The tests were accomplished in the persons' homes, and great care was taken to work only under what seemed to be psychologically favorable conditions. During the tests the paper tape recorder was connected to the RNG and the electromechanical reset and non-reset counters for the numbers of hits and trials were switched on. Between tests, the subjects were allowed to play with the RNG, in particular, in order to determine their momentary efficiency in predicting. During these play periods the paper tape puncher and the non-reset counters were disconnected. It was decided in advance to evaluate all and only the events recorded on tape.

The tests were taken on many different days. The number of trials to be made on each day was determined by the subject's and the experimenter's mood and time availability. The total number of trials to be made in the first main experiments was specified in advance as being more than 55,000 and less than 70,000; the actual number of trials made, determined by external circumstances, was 63,066.

The equipment was so designed that the presence of the experimenter during the tests was not necessary: Forging the records by the subject would have required opening the sealed RNG, advancing the non-reset counters by electrical impulses, and punching of properly coded holes into the paper tape. The writer was present, however, during all tests with the exception of some with O.C. in the first main experiment.

On eleven days (between February 20 and March 9, 1967) 22,569 trials were made with the first subject, Mr. O.C., and 285.75 hits over the expected number were obtained. This number of hits lies by 4.39 standard deviations above the expectation value. Figure 1 shows the increase of the score with the number of trials.

Mathematical analysis of the sequence of numbers generated by the RNG during the tests suggests a non-randomness in this sequence.

One more control test pertaining to the randomness may be mentioned here. Since the paper tape contains the whole sequence of the numbers predicted by O.C. (i.e., the sequence in which he pressed the buttons), the buttons of the RNG could be activated automatically in the same sequence in which O.C. had pressed them, but with different input speeds. Ten such control runs were made. The numbers of hits above average obtained here ($+5$, $+4$, -53, $+13$, $+54$, $+28$, $+73$, $+5$, -20, -36) are not significantly high.

Tests were made on five days (between March 22 and April 7, 1967) with the second subject, Mrs. J.B. Out of $N=16,250$ trials, 90.5 more hits than expected were obtained, 1.64 standard deviations above the expectation value. Figure 1 shows the increase of the score with the number of trials. Again, mathematical tests do not indicate a non-randomness.

In preliminary tests the third subject, Mr. K.M.R., had used two different approaches for obtaining high scores. In some tests he waited for some intuition concerning the next light and then pressed the corresponding button. In other tests, however, he concentrated on the red lamp (the colors were blue, green, orange, red), waited until he felt that the red light would appear, and then pressed the button next to the red lamp.

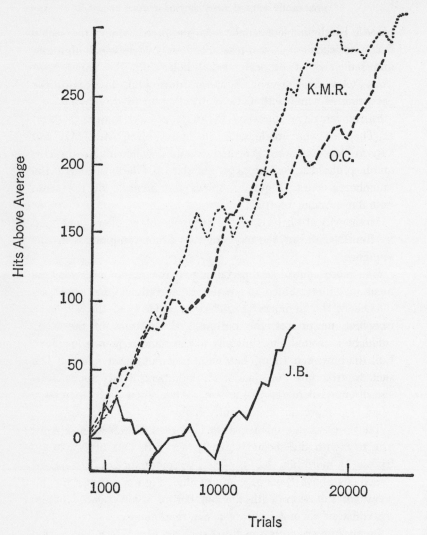

Figure 1

Hits Above Average
in First Experiment

K.M.R. used the latter approach during his whole part in the main experiment. Thus in this test only the "red" button was pressed at times determined by the subject, and his objective was "to catch many red lights" (i.e., to obtain in the sequence of generated numbers many 4s, since number 4 corresponds to the red lamp).

The test was done in two sessions (23,247 trials on April 19–20, 1000 trials on May 24, 1967). The increase of the score with progressing number of trials is given in Figure 1. The number 4 occurred significantly more frequently than the other numbers; more than 300 hits above the expected were observed.

Randomness tests were performed directly before (23,600 numbers) and directly after (50,000 numbers) the long session and directly after (142,000 numbers) the short session; there was no indication of non-randomness in the mechanism.

One of the subjects from the previous test (K.M.R.) had become unavailable and was replaced by S.C. (sixteen-year-old daughter of O.C.) in a portion of the second main experiment. As in the previous experiment the subject was seated in front of the box with four colored lamps and four corresponding push buttons. In the present experiment, however, the subjects had the option either to predict which lamp would light next and to press the corresponding button (try for high score) or to try to select one lamp which would not light and to press that button (try for low score). At the beginning of each session it was decided whether to try for a high or a low score. The two modes of operation were recorded on tape in different codes so that the evaluating computer could separate the two types of test.

Between September 6 and November 29, 1967, four sessions were made with O.C., eleven sessions with J.B., and six sessions with S.C. The results are summarized in Figure 2. O.C. tried for high score only, J.B. partly for high and partly for low, and S.C. tried for low score only. It was decided in advance to evaluate in this experiment the total number of either 20,000

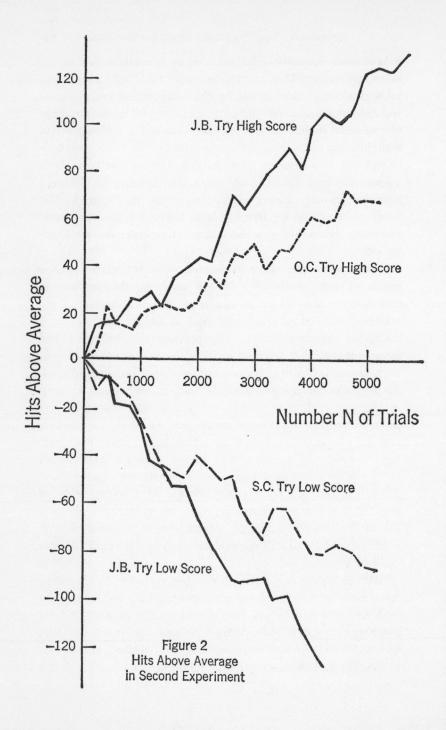

Figure 2
Hits Above Average
in Second Experiment

or 40,000 trials. Actually 20,000 trials were made and 401 hits above the expected value were achieved.

Large series of random numbers were generated before, after, and between the sessions for inclusion in mathematical randomness tests. In particular, directly after each of the eleven sessions with J.B., approximately 100,000 such numbers were recorded; these tests do not suggest non-random behavior.

From Figures 1 and 2 it seems fairly obvious that the consistently high scores of the selected subjects are not just the result of a statistical chance fluctuation. To corroborate this impression the probabilities for obtaining these or higher scores by chance alone can be calculated: For the the first experiment the probability of chance alone being responsible for the results is less than one in 500 million; for the second set the probability is less than one in 10 billion.

The results seem to indicate that some subjects do have the ability to predict the random numbers better than quantum theory permits.

There might appear to be other, less drastic, explanations of the high number of hits recorded as:

1) Recording errors.
2) High score as a result of statistical chance fluctuation.
3) High score as a result of non-randomness of the target sequence.

Let us review these points separately:

1. The numbers of hits and trials were recorded independently by internal counters and by the punch tape. These records did agree. The recording was safe against possible fraud by the subject and negligence of the experimenter. In particular, negligently selective reporting was ruled out by evaluating everything recorded on tape during the tests.

2. Particular efforts were made to continue the tests sufficiently long so as to obtain results well above the statistical fluctuations. The high statistical significance of the results excludes the possibility that the high scores were obtained as a result of chance alone.

3. The random numbers are generated with the help of conventional solid state digital electronics, combined with a Geiger-Mueller tube exposed to beta radiation. A theoretical estimate shows that the sequence of generated numbers is sufficiently random and determined by quantum processes, provided that no gross malfunction of the electronics occurs. The circuitry suggests that any such malfunction should lead to a change in the generation rate of either one number or a pair of two successively generated numbers. Experimental tests for randomness were designed to detect such temporary or permanent changes of generation rate. These tests (comprising a number of counts seventy-five times as large as the number of trials made in the precognition tests) were conducted preferably directly before or after the precognition tests in order to minimize the probability that the generator should happen to perform properly during all randomness tests, but improperly during the precognition tests. The randomness tests as well as the direct checks of the electronic operation did not suggest any non-randomness.

Thus, it seems that these alternate explanations can be ruled out with reasonable confidence.

The purpose of the reported experiments was to check the existence of a phenomenon which was called "anomalous prediction of quantum processes." More generally this phenomenon might be interpreted as an anomalous (not yet understood) correlation between the subject and the random number generator.

10

O. G. VILLARD, JR.,

C. R. GRAF, *and*

J. M. LOMASNEY

Long Delayed Echoes
of Radio Transmissions

Some radio operators, hams, are engaged in an exciting search for information about a phenomenon which has eluded scientific explanation. Sometimes, on very rare occasions, hams hear their own transmissions on their receivers after they have stopped transmitting. The time delay between their transmission and the "echo" is too long to be accounted for by easy explanations such as circling of the earth by the radio signal or reflections from the moon. As the data accumulates, perhaps some explanation consistent with our current ideas of radio will emerge. If explanations cannot be found, revisions to the theory of radio propagation may be required.

The authors of the following article are all radio amateurs professionally engaged in radio propagation research. The piece, which originally appeared in the magazine QST, the publication of the American Radio Relay League, requested the help of hams worldwide to record and report radio-echo observa-

*tions in the future. They wrote as hams to hams and one can
sense the excitement of the search.*

Have you ever had the experience of hearing your own voice
repeat the last couple of words of your transmission, after you
have switched over to receive? Or have you been aware, after
another station stands by, that a weaker signal on the same
frequency is repeating the last few words of the transmission,
with exactly the same "fist"?

Well, believe it or not, some amateurs have. If you, dear
reader, think us out of our minds to even bring this matter
up, rest assured that there are many others who share your
view and would cheerfully consign us to the booby hatch.
If you haven't tuned out by now, you are undoubtedly asking:
Just who *are* the folk who have had this experience? Are they
emotionally unstable types, prone to LSD-style hallucination?
But hear this: One is a professor of mathematics at a well-
known West Coast university; another is a physicist at a Mid-
west research foundation; still another has managerial responsibility for important communication satellite programs at a
prominent West Coast aerospace corporation, and most of the
rest have a professional connection with electronics in some
way. . . .

Hard to discount their reports, it appears. Were these men
hoaxed, you ask? That's always a possibility, and it apparently
has happened in the past. But what about the instances where
the echo was heard *both* on the ham's own signal, *and* on
the signal of the station being worked? It would take a pretty
clever spoof to simulate both the sound of long-distance transmission and the transmit-receive timing. Still, it could be done,
just as a photograph of a flying saucer can be handily simulated
with the aid of ordinary crockery.

That's what makes the study of long-delay echoes (LDEs)
exciting. At the moment, there is no really indisputable proof

that they exist. Scientists remain unconvinced about UFOs, and LDEs are in the same category. However, an increasing body of experimental evidence argues for the reality of LDEs, and it is interesting that a number of new ideas for possible theoretical explanations have come to light only within the last couple of years.

Scientific research is placed under great handicaps when the effect being studied is highly infrequent in occurrence. The handicap is even worse when there is no satisfactory theory to guide experimentation. In these circumstances it hardly pays to set up a special test if a useful result is achieved only once a year on the average. This problem is well known to astronomers, who depend almost entirely on amateur reports to locate comets which pop into view in unannounced places and at unannounced times. Busy professionals simply cannot devote that many hours per year to scanning the skies. LDEs provide an analogous opportunity for hams to be of service to the professional community. Reports on LDEs, with time logged accurately, should be invaluable in helping to solve this particular puzzle.

BACKGROUND

Echoes of very long delay were first reported in 1928 (References 1 and 2), not long after international short-wave broadcasting got under way. Transmitter powers were around ten kilowatts; antennas were tilted wires; the radio frequency used was around ten megacycles, and receivers were for the most part regenerative. Oscilloscopes and tape recorders were unheard of. On the other hand, interference levels were far below those of today. The experiment consisted of transmitting one or more dots or dashes, and timing the received signals with the aid of a stop watch. Delays ranged from two to thirty seconds. Echoes were heard at locations both close to and distant from the transmitter, sometimes apparently at the same time. Figure 1 shows an example.

A number of theories in explanation of the observations were tried and discarded. The basic difficulty is that radio waves in most circumstances travel at the velocity of light (186,000 miles per second), so that a complete transit of the earth takes only one seventh of a second. A trip to the moon and back takes roughly two seconds. One theory held that the waves might be slowed down sufficiently if they happened to be close to the ionospheric "critical frequency"; however, it soon became obvious that the accompanying losses would inevitably swallow them up. Loss also makes the possibility of multiple passes around the earth unlikely (210 are required for a thirty-second delay)—for the ionospheric gas is by its very nature a lossy dielectric. The hypothesis that echoes might be returned from uncharted clouds of electrons far distant from the earth was seriously considered at the time: today, of course, we know that deep space holds no surprises of that particular sort.

By the middle 1930s few echoes were being received, and the matter remained dormant until the Cavendish Laboratory of Cambridge University undertook a study in 1948 (Reference 3). In a careful year-long test involving transmission of about 27,000 test signals at 13.4 and 20.6 MHz., not one LDE was recorded. No further published scientific activity seems to have taken place since that time. In the intervening years there appears to have been at least one amateur report which was discovered to be a hoax, and in another instance a mechanical fault in a recording was responsible for reports of "delayed echoes" audible on a standard-frequency-station time announcement.

In scientific work when none of the postulated explanations satisfactorily explains a reported effect, and when a reputable scientific organization attempts to find it experimentally and doesn't succeed, there is an understandable and almost overpowering impulse on the part of other members of the scientific fraternity *not* to become further involved. This is how LDEs came to have roughly the same dubious status as UFOs.

MORE RECENT EXPERIMENTS

In 1958, W5LFM* drew W6QYT's attention to field-strength recordings in which there was an apparent decay of received-signal energy during the thirty-second interval of carrier interruption for identification purposes. This behavior, which *could* have been ascribed to weak (perhaps incoherent) long-delayed echo energy, turned out in the end to be due to the effect of mechanical "stiction" on operation of the pens of the then-standard Esterline-Angus paper-chart recorders. The observation did, however, suggest an inexpensive means for collecting data on possible LDEs: Use a more suitable recorder and see what is left behind on the frequency when WWV's carriers leave the air once an hour. Studies of this sort were made by W6QYT with the help of various part-time graduate-student assistants at Stanford University in the period 1958–60 (Reference 4). The following suspicious circumstances were—very occasionally—noted:

1) extra noise, decaying exponentially for tens of seconds,

2) extra noise of roughly constant intensity, enduring for about the same period of time, and

3) instances where the same noise actually contained a weak signal similar to the WWV carrier. Some eighteen of the type 3 events were observed in a period of about a year. These findings were reported to the Office of Naval Research under whose contract the work was performed, but they were never published because it could not be proved beyond reasonable doubt that the observed signals were in reality caused by the WWV transmissions. They could, for example, have been the result of an obscure fault in the transmitter, although this is considered highly unlikely. WWV frequencies are shared by other standard-frequency stations throughout the world; this introduces troublesome uncertainty. (So does harmonic radiation from 100-kHz.

* W5LFM is an amateur's call letters.

crystal oscillators on the Hewlett-Packard Palo Alto production line, as WB6FDV found out in a classic bit of detective work.) A more sophisticated experiment was clearly needed to decide the matter one way or another, and the effort was sidetracked owing to the pressure of other activities.

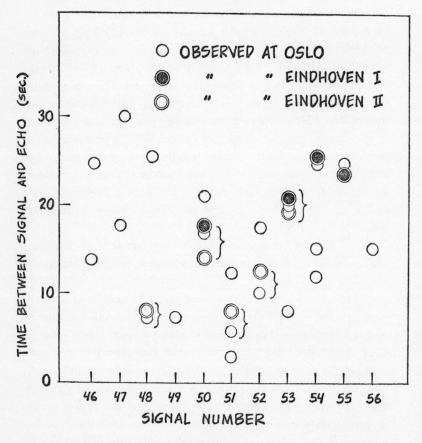

FIGURE 1

Some early observations of long-delayed echoes, some of which were apparently audible at three locations at the same time. Signals were sent every 30 seconds; note the briefness of the total period of reception. (From Reference 2.)

POSSIBLE THEORETICAL EXPLANATIONS

If high frequency signals are to endure for tens of seconds, a way must be found for ionospheric loss to be overcome. In the 1930s, the possibility of signal amplification in the ionosphere had not occurred to anyone, but today we can visualize a number of means by which this might take place. Parametric amplification has been suggested (Reference 5): The ionosphere is not a perfectly linear dielectric, and if we could exploit this property, one signal—in principle—could "pump" another. Another new development is maser amplification; the ionospheric plasma is acted upon by a whole spectrum of radiation from the sun; is it possible that amplification-producing population inversion somehow takes place? Still another explanation has to do with signal storage in the ordered motion of electrons spinning around magnetic field lines; for example, there might be an ionospheric analogue of the phenomenon of spin echoes in nuclear magnetic resonance.

Professor F. W. Crawford of Stanford University has been studying—on paper and in the laboratory—plasmas that "talk back," almost like Edison's original phonograph (Reference 6). A complex signal is fed in, which then disappears insofar as the external circuit is concerned. To call it out, the plasma is pulsed; a replica *reversed in time* then appears. These "plasmas with memory"—and the above is only one scheme of many —are most readily studied when comparatively high pressures and gigahertz radio frequencies are used. The tantalizing feature of these experiments is that if they *could* be extended to ionospheric pressures and high frequencies, the indicated time delays fall right in the 3–30 second ball park.

Another remarkable and comparatively recent finding is the so-called "stimulated natural emission" observable at very low frequencies. At these frequencies (on the order of 15 kHz.), radio signals both travel underneath the ionosphere and penetrate it. Those which penetrate are guided by the magnetic field lines and travel from northern to southern hemispheres at phenomenally high altitudes over the equator (one or two earth radii). During their travel, these waves actually rearrange the ambient electrons and store energy in them. This energy is available to amplify any signals of the same frequency after the causative wave is shut off. As a result, an unstable but recognizable replica of the signal is heard after the original transmission stops. This mechanism most emphatically will *not* work at high frequency, since the circumstances are then wholly different. But the fact that radio signal amplification in the ionosphere can happen at all makes the possibility that something analogous might happen at high frequency seem more likely.

These new developments in the understanding of plasmas stimulated W6QYT to ask for reports of LDEs at a recent get-together of the Northern and Southern California DX Clubs; to his surprise five excellent ones were received; they are included in the summary below.

W5LFM, who has also been interested in this subject since 1958, has collected reports from W5VY and W5LUU, and has

Summary of LDE Reports

DATE	CALL	BAND, MHZ.	APPROX. DURATION, SECONDS	TIME, GMT	PHONE/ C.W.	AUDIBLE ON OWN/OTHER
Oct. 16, 1932	W6ADP	28	18	≈1800	c.w.	Own
Winter, 1950–51	W5LUU	7	5	≈0300	c.w.	Own
Winter, 1965	K6EV	14	3–4	0600–0700	s.s.b.	Own
Dec. 2, 1967	W5VY	28	3	1328	s.s.b.	Own
Jan. 27, 1968	W5LFM	10	½	1400–1430	Time Ticks	Station RID
Dec. 18, 1968	W6KPC	28	1	≈2000	s.s.b.	Other
Jan. 21, 1969	W6OL	14	6–10	1536	c.w.	Other
Feb. 17, 1969	K6CAZ	2	≈2	1430–1500	s.s.b.	Own and Other

himself observed a difficult-to-explain half-second time delay on the time ticks of a Russian standard-frequency station.

SUMMARY OF CHARACTERISTICS

The Stanford recordings suggested—but did not prove—that incoherent noise "echoes" may exist, as well as coherent ones containing a replica of the signal. The amateur and the early reports, of course, deal only with the coherent variety, which seem to be appreciably less frequent in occurrence. Following is a summary of the conclusions which can be derived from the ham reports taken as a group:

1) Multiple-second "coherent" signal echoes, either phone or code, appear to be real, and are observable for short periods of time at highly infrequent intervals.

2) They are audible both on a station's own signals and on signals of other stations.

3) They have been observed at 7, 14, 21, and 28 MHz., but apparently not at higher frequencies,

4) They either occur most frequently (or perhaps are most easily heard) when a given band is just "opening up" —i.e., when skywave propagation to some point on earth is just becoming possible.

5) They seem to be audible when long-distance propagation is good, and when geomagnetic activity is low. (The presence of long-path as well as short-path propagation, or signals from stations at antipodal locations, is apparently a good omen.)

6) Stations reporting LDEs typically have been ones having antennas well up in the air, at locations reasonably good for long-distance transmissions, but other than that no exceptional facilities seem to be required.

7) An active ham who transmits to distant stations one or two hours a day, may expect to hear an LDE once a year, on the average.

8) The LDEs appear to be one single echo, rather than several successive ones.

9) No Doppler shift is perceptible.

10) The sound of the echo resembles that of a distant signal (i.e., it apparently involves long-distance multipath propagation.)

11) The strength is usually weak, although some reports have put it well above the noise.

12) Echo strength always decays with time, rather than the other way around.

13) The total time interval during which the echo effect can be heard is remarkably short—usually no more than a few minutes.

14) There is some indication that LDEs may be heard more frequently on signals which have traveled through the northern and southern auroral zones.

A COMPARISON

It isn't clear that the currently-observed effect is the same thing as was reported in the 1930s, since the early accounts all stressed a multiplicity of signals returned for a single outgoing pulse. But a connection is certainly possible.

It is interesting to compare the circumstances of the experiments of those times with those of today. The early work involved high-transmitter power (10 kw. or so), relatively nondirectional antennas (tilted wires) radiating upward as well as outward, frequencies of the order of 10 MHz., and comparatively short-distance propagation. Today's observations were performed with lower power, higher beam gain, higher frequencies, antennas directing their energy closer to the horizon, and long-distance propagation.

As the Cambridge group (Reference 7) pointed out, perhaps the most significant difference between "then" and "now" is the greater crowding of the high-frequency spectrum. In their view their lack of results might in part be explained by the difficulty of finding a clear channel. It is certainly true that they operated in commercial telegraphy bands, which are comparatively crowded; it is also true that their antennas were directive upward, since they were primarily looking for reflections from electron clouds in space. It is also possible to speculate that if maser amplification were involved, interference would have the effect of siphoning off amplifying power which might otherwise go into keeping the echo going. (This would be in addition to the obscuring effect of the interference.) The QRM would tend to be amplified, instead of the echo, since stimulated electrons in giving up their energy will tend to lock themselves to the strongest signals of the appropriate frequency present at any given time.

WHAT AMATEURS CAN DO TO HELP

Additional amateur reports of LDEs are urgently needed to guide on-going research. If an LDE *is* experienced, the most important single piece of information to write down is the exact time of occurrence. Because LDEs are so transitory, it may be possible to establish a relationship to other, equally transistory geophysical events simply by making a time-of-occurrence comparison. Try to log, *at the time*, all the circumstances of the experimental setup—frequency, antenna heading, etc., plus a careful description of the observed effect.

It is suggested that the making of special transmissions in the hope of catching an LDE is a sure road to total frustration. Best bet is to act as if they didn't exist. However, if you have a tape recorder which can be spared from other duty, use it to record the output of the station receiver at all times. A single tape can be used over and over again. Then, should an echo put in an appearance, you'll have it trapped—if the tape hasn't worn out in the meantime! Frequency-amplitude-time plots (similar to "voice prints"), made from such recordings, should be very instructive. However, tapes (like photos of UFOs) can be easily faked, so don't expect to convince skeptical scientists and garner instant glory by producing a single example: Nobody will bite. Nevertheless, many tapes collected over a period of time at many locations and containing internally consistent information may well permit the piecing together of a sensible explanation.

It's fun to think that in this era of "big" science there is still an area where amateur radio operators can make contributions which will be as uniquely valuable as those provided to astronomers by the amateur comet watchers.

SOME REACTIONS UPON HEARING LDES

Those who are privileged to hear LDEs are clearly members of a highly exclusive club, since many hams active for twenty years or more have never observed anything like it. Yet some who do, such as W5VY and W6CAZ, report that they hear LDEs on the average about once a year when they are operating regularly (perhaps 1–2 hours per day on the average). Hence, the effect must happen at least this often.

W6QYT has queried ship-to-shore radio-telegraph operators of the Mackay Radio receiving site at Half Moon Bay, California, with negative results. It appears that these men, who contact ships at varying distances throughout the world, every day, around the clock, and in several wave bands, simply do not hear LDEs. However, a typical ship transmitter has a power in the order of 150 watts, and a non-directional antenna; hence it is not as potent as most ham stations.

Psychologists say that the human mental computer is astonishingly efficient at recognizing something which is known. This is probably an important aspect in the identification of one's own voice or "fist." One wonders how many weak LDEs associated with other transmissions may have gone unnoticed, because the ear tends to shut out—automatically—anything it classes as QRM, and therefore spurious.

The almost universal reaction to hearing a good LDE is total astonishment. For this reason the memory tends to be fresh even after the passage of years. Some of the reports convey this feeling quite dramatically. According to W6OL, "I was just tuning the band, listening, and heard this Russian working someone. There was some slight interference on his transmission but the copy was reasonably good. However, I heard him sign and then I realized that the interference was his echo, and that I could again copy the last part of the transmission." Says W6KPC, who heard "whole words, if they were not too long . . . the echo was so loud, long, and startling that my reaction was to 'talk' about it with someone! . . . I've never heard such long echoes before or since." In W6ADP's words, "I was calling ON4AU on 28 Mc. and switched over to listen and heard on my own frequency ON4AU de W6ADP K. Was very weird and never will forget it. Signal sounded like it was coming a long way but was S6 or so."

ACKNOWLEDGMENT

The assistance of Professor B. Dueno, KP4HF, is gratefully acknowledged. Members of the staff of WWV and WWVH have provided useful information. Measurements at Stanford University were supported in part by the Office of Naval Research under contracts Nonr-225(24) and Nonr-225(64).

REFERENCES

1. C. Stormer, *Nature*, 122, 1928, p. 681.

2. B. Van der Pol, *Nature*, 122, Dec. 1928, pp. 878–79.

3. K. G. Budden and G. G. Yates, "A Search for Radio Echoes of Long Delay," *Jour. of Atmos. and Terr. Physics*, 2, 1952, pp. 272–81.

4. Quarterly Status Reports, Tri-Service Contract Nonr-225(24) NR. 373 360, Stanford Electronics Laboratories, Stanford, Calif. See reports 17–25, covering the period Oct. 1958–Dec. 1960.

5. K. J. Harker, and F. W. Crawford, Stanford University Institute for Plasma Research, Report No. 264, Dec. 1968.

6. F. W. Crawford, "A New Look at Very Long Delayed Radio Echoes," Combined Session, URSI Spring Meeting, Apr. 1968.

7. Budden and Yates, op. cit.

11

I. L. HOROWITZ

The Life and Death
of Project Camelot

Camelot was a social science project designed to develop methods for forecasting the occurrence of revolutions and to influence social change (presumably in directions favorable to the United States) in developing countries. It was sponsored by the Department of Defense and represented "big science" to the political scientists and sociologists it engaged. The project ended traumatically in 1965 admidst bickering over political jurisdiction and ethical introspection. Should a self-respecting social scientist take money from the Department of Defense? Was the Department of Defense sponsoring research in the interests of broader science or was it trying to further the military and political interests of the country?

Clearly, Camelot raised important questions about the frontier between government and science. The eminent sociologist Dr. Irving Horowitz has chronicled the saga of Camelot in the next piece, which originally appeared in the November/December 1965 issue of the journal Transaction.

In June of 1965—in the midst of the crisis over the Dominican Republic—the United States Ambassador to Chile sent an urgent and angry cable to the State Department. Ambassador Ralph Dungan was confronted with a growing outburst of anti-Americanism from Chilean newspapers and intellectuals. Further, left-wing members of the Chilean Senate had accused the United States of espionage.

The anti-American attacks that agitated Dungan had no direct connection with sending U.S. troops to Santo Domingo. Their target was a mysterious and cloudy American research program called Project Camelot.

Dungan wanted to know from the State Department what Project Camelot was all about. Further, whatever Camelot was, he wanted it stopped because it was fast becoming a *cause célèbre* in Chile (as it soon would throughout capitals of Latin America and in Washington) and Dungan had not been told anything about it—even though it was sponsored by the U. S. Army and involved the tinderbox subjects of counterrevolution and counterinsurgency in Latin America.

Within a few weeks Project Camelot created repercussions from Capitol Hill to the White House. Senator J. William Fulbright, chairman of the Foreign Relations Committee, registered his personal concern about such projects as Camelot because of their "reactionary, backward-looking policy opposed to change. Implicit in Camelot, as in the concept of 'counterinsurgency,' is an assumption that revolutionary movements are dangerous to the interests of the United States and that the United States must be prepared to assist, if not actually to participate in, measures to repress them."

By mid-June the State Department and Defense Department—which had created and funded Camelot—were in open contention over the project and the jurisdiction each department should have over certain foreign policy operations.

On July 8, Project Camelot was killed by Defense Secretary Robert McNamara's office which has a veto power over the military budget. The decision had been made under the President's direction.

On that same day, the director of Camelot's parent body, the Special Operations Research Organization, told a congressional committee that the research project on revolution and counterinsurgency had taken its name from King Arthur's mythical domain because "It connotes the right sort of things—development of a stable society with peace and justice for all." Whatever Camelot's outcome, there should be no mistaking the deep sincerity behind this appeal for an applied social science pertinent to current policy.

However, Camelot left a horizon of disarray in its wake; an open dispute between State and Defense; fuel for the anti-American fires in Latin America; a cut in U. S. Army research appropriations. In addition, serious and perhaps ominous implications for social science research, bordering on censorship, have been raised by the heated reaction of the executive branch of government.

GLOBAL COUNTERINSURGENCY

What was Project Camelot? Basically, it was a project for measuring and forecasting the causes of revolutions and insurgency in underdeveloped areas of the world. It also aimed to find ways of eliminating the causes, or coping with the revolutions and insurgencies. Camelot was sponsored by the U. S. Army on a four to six million dollar contract, spaced out over three to four years, with the Special Operations Research Organization (SORO). This agency is nominally under the aegis of American University in Washington, D.C., and does a variety of research for the Army. This includes making analytical surveys of foreign areas; keeping up-to-date information on the military, political, and social complexes of those areas; and maintaining a "rapid response" file for getting immediate information, upon Army request, on any situation deemed militarily important.

Latin America was the first area chosen for concentrated study, but countries on Camelot's four-year list included some in Asia, Africa, and Europe. In a working paper issued on December 5, 1964, at the request of the Office of the Chief of Research and Development, Department of the Army, it was recommended that "comparative historical studies" be made in these countries:

- (Latin America) Argentina, Bolivia, Brazil, Colombia, Cuba, Dominican Republic, El Salvador, Guatemala, Mexico, Paraguay, Peru, Venezuela.
- (Middle East) Egypt, Iran, Turkey.
- (Far East) Korea, Indonesia, Malaysia, Thailand.
- (Others) France, Greece, Nigeria.

"Survey research and other field studies" were recommended for Bolivia, Colombia, Ecuador, Paraguay, Peru, Venezuela, Iran, Thailand. Preliminary consideration was also being given to a study of the separatist movement in French Canada. It, too, had a code name: Project Revolt.

In a recruiting letter sent to selected scholars all over the world at the end of 1964, Project Camelot's aims were defined as a study to "make it possible to predict and influence politically significant aspects of social change in the developing nations of the world." This would include devising procedures for "assessing the potential for internal war within national societies" and "identify(ing) with increased degrees of confidence, those actions which a government might take to relieve conditions which are assessed as giving rise to a potential for internal war." The letter further stated:

The US Army has an important mission in the positive and constructive aspects of nation-building in less developed countries as well as a responsibility to assist friendly governments in dealing with active insurgency problems.

Such activities by the U. S. Army were described as "insurgency prophylaxis" rather than the "sometimes misleading label of counterinsurgency."

Project Camelot was conceived in late 1963 by a group of high-ranking Army officers connected with the Army Research Office of the Department of Defense. They were concerned about new types of warfare springing up around the world. Revolutions in Cuba and Yemen and insurgency movements in Vietnam and the Congo were a far cry from the battles of World War II and also different from the envisioned—and planned for—apocalypse of nuclear war. For the first time in modern warfare, military establishments were not in a position to use the immense arsenals at their disposal—but were, instead, compelled by force of a geopolitical stalemate to increasingly engage in primitive forms of armed combat. The questions of moment for the Army were: Why can't the "hardware" be used? And what alternatives can social science "software" provide?

A well-known Latin American area specialist, Rex Hopper, was chosen as director of Project Camelot. Hopper was a professor of sociology and chairman of the department at Brooklyn College. He had been to Latin America many times over a thirty-year span on research projects and lecture tours, including some under government sponsorship. He was highly recommended for the position by his professional associates in Washington and elsewhere. Hopper had a long-standing interest in problems of revolution and saw in this multimillion-dollar contract the possible realization of a life-long scientific ambition.

THE CHILEAN DEBACLE

How did this social science research project create a foreign policy furore? And, at another level, how did such high intentions result in so disastrous an outcome?

The answers involve a network spreading from a professor of anthropology at the University of Pittsburgh, to a professor of sociology at the University of Oslo, and yet a third professor of sociology at the University of Chile in Santiago, Chile. The "showdown" took place in Chile, first within the confines of the university, next on the floor of the Chilean Senate, then in the popular press of Santiago, and finally, behind U.S. embassy walls.

It was ironic that Chile was the scene of wild newspaper tales of spying and academic outrage at scholars being recruited for "spying missions." For the working papers of Project Camelot stipulated as a criterion for study that a country "should show promise of high pay-offs in terms of the kinds of data required." Chile did not meet these requirements—it is not on the preliminary list of nations specified as prospects.

How then did Chile become involved in Project Camelot's affairs? The answer requires consideration of the position of Hugo G. Nutini, assistant professor of anthropology at Pittsburgh, citizen of the United States and former citizen of Chile. His presence in Santiago as a self-identified Camelot representative triggered the climactic chain of events.

Nutini, who inquired about an appointment in Camelot's beginning stages, never was given a regular Camelot appointment. Because he was planning a trip to Chile in April of this year—on other academic business—he was asked to prepare a report concerning possibilities of cooperation from Chilean scholars. In general, it was the kind of survey which has mild results and a modest honorarium attached to it (Nutini was offered $750). But Nutini had an obviously different notion of his role. Despite the limitations and precautions which Rex Hopper placed on his trip, especially Hopper's insistence on its informal nature, Nutini managed to convey the impression of being an official of Project Camelot with the authority to make proposals to prospective Chilean participants. Here was an opportunity to link the country of his birth with the country of his choice.

At about the same time, Johan Galtung, a Norwegian sociologist famous for his research on conflict and conflict resolution in underdeveloped areas, especially in Latin America, entered the picture. Galtung, who was in Chile at the time and associated with the Latin American Faculty of Social

Science (FLACSO), received in invitation to participate in a Camelot planning conference scheduled for Washington, D.C., in August 1965. The fee to social scientists attending the conference would be $2000 for four weeks. Galtung turned down the invitation. He gave several reasons. He could not accept the role of the U. S. Army as a sponsoring agent in a study of counterinsurgency. He could not accept the notion of the Army as an agency of national development; he saw the Army as managing conflict and even promoting conflict. Finally, he could not accept the asymmetry of the project—he found it difficult to understand why there would be studies of counterinsurgency in Latin America, but no studies of "counterintervention" (conditions under which Latin American nations might intervene in the affairs of the United States). Galtung was also deeply concerned about the possibility of European scholars being frozen out of Latin American studies by an inundation of sociologists from the United States. Furthermore, he expressed fears that the scale of Camelot honoraria would completely destroy the social science labor market in Latin America.

Galtung had spoken to others in Oslo, Santiago, and throughout Latin America about the project, and he had shown the memorandum of December 1964 to many of his colleagues.

Soon after Nutini arrived in Santiago, he had a conference with Vice-Chancellor Alvaro Bunster of the University of Chile to discuss the character of Project Camelot. Their second meeting, arranged by the vice-chancellor, was also attended by Professor Eduardo Fuenzalida, a sociologist. After a half hour of exposition by Nutini, Fuenzalida asked him point-blank to specify the ultimate aims of the project, its sponsors, and its military implications. Before Nutini could reply, Professor Fuenzalida, apparently with some drama, pulled a copy of the December 4 circular letter from his briefcase and read a prepared Spanish translation. Simultaneously, the authorities at FLACSO turned over the matter to their associates in the Chilean Senate and in the left-wing Chilean press.

In Washington, under the political pressures of State Department officials and congressional reaction, Project Camelot was halted in midstream, or more precisely, before it ever really got under way. When the ambassador's communication reached Washington, there was already considerable official ferment about Project Camelot. Senators Fulbright, Morse, and McCarthy soon asked for hearings by the Senate Foreign Relations Committee. Only an agreement between Secretary of Defense McNamara and Secretary of State Rusk to settle their differences on future overseas research projects forestalled Senate action. But in the House of Representatives, a hearing was conducted by the Foreign Affairs Committee on July 8. The SORO director, Theodore Vallance, was questioned by committee members on the worth of Camelot and the matter of military intrusion into foreign policy areas.

That morning, even before Vallance was sworn in as a witness —and without his knowledge—the Defense Department issued a terse announcement terminating Project Camelot. President Johnson had decided to issue in favor of the State Department. In a memo to Secretary Rusk on August 5, the President stipulated that "no government sponsorship of foreign area research should be undertaken which in the judgment of the Secretary of State would adversely affect United States foreign relations."

The State Department has recently established machinery to screen and judge all federally financed research projects overseas. The policy and research consequences of the presidential directive will be discussed later.

What effect will the cancellation of Camelot have on the continuing rivalry between Defense and State departments for primacy in foreign policy? How will government sponsorship of future social science research be affected? And was Project Camelot a scholarly protective cover for U. S. Army planning—or a legitimate research operation on a valid research subject independent of sponsorship?

Let us begin with a collective self-portrait of Camelot as

the social scientists who directed the project perceived it. There seems to be general consensus on seven points.

▪ First, the men who went to work for Camelot felt the need for a large-scale, "big picture" project in social science. They wanted to create a sociology of contemporary relevance which would not suffer from the parochial narrowness of vision to which their own professional backgrounds had generally conditioned them. Most of the men viewed Camelot as a bona fide opportunity to do fundamental research with relatively unlimited funds at their disposal. (No social science project ever before had up to $6,000,000 available.) Under such optimal conditions, these scholars tended not to look a gift horse in the mouth. As one of them put it, there was no desire to inquire too deeply as to the source of the funds or the ultimate purpose of the project.

▪ Second, most social scientists affiliated with Camelot felt that there was actually more freedom to do fundamental research under military sponsorship than at a university or college. One man noted that during the 1950s there was far more freedom to do fundamental research in the RAND corporation (an Air Force research organization) than on any campus in America. Indeed, once the protective covering of RAND was adopted, it was almost viewed as a society of Platonist elites or "knowers" permitted to search for truth on behalf of the powerful. In a neoplatonic definition of their situation, the Camelot men hoped that their ideas would be taken seriously by the wielders of power (although, conversely, they were conceived that the armed forces would not accept their preliminary recommendations).

▪ Third, many of the Camelot associates felt distinctly uncomfortable with military sponsorship, especially given the present United States military posture. But their reaction to this discomfort was that "the Army has to be educated." This view was sometimes cast in Freudian terms: The Army's bent toward violence ought to be sublimated. Underlying this theme was the notion of the armed forces as an agency for potential social good—the discipline and the order embodied by an army could be channeled into the process of economic and social development in the United States as well as in Latin America.

▪ Fourth, there was a profound conviction in the perfectibility of mankind; particularly in the possibility of the military establishment performing a major role in the general process of growth. They sought to correct the intellectual paternalism and parochialism under which Pentagon generals, State Department diplomats, and Defense Department planners seemed to operate.

▪ Fifth, a major long-range purpose of Camelot, at least for some of its policy makers, was to prevent another revolutionary holocaust on a grand scale, such as occurred in Cuba. At the very least, there was a shared belief that *Pax Americana* was severely threatened and its future could be bolstered.

▪ Sixth, none of them viewed their role on the project as spying for the United States Government, or for anyone else.

▪ Seventh, the men on Project Camelot felt that they made heavy sacrifices for social science. Their personal and professional risks were much higher than those taken by university academics. Government work, while well-compensated, remains professionally marginal. It can be terminated abruptly (as indeed was the case) and its project directors are subject to a public scrutiny not customary behind the walls of ivy.

In the main, there was perhaps a keener desire on the part of the directing members of Camelot not to "sell out" than there is among social scientists with regular academic appointments. This concern with the ethics of social science research seemed to be due largely to daily confrontation of the problems of betrayal, treason, secrecy, and abuse of data, in a critical situation. In contrast, even though a university position may be created by federally sponsored research, the connection with policy matters is often too remote to cause any *crise de conscience.*

THE INSIDERS REPORT

Were the men on Camelot critical of any aspects of the project?

Some had doubts from the outset about the character of the work they would be doing and about the conditions under which it would be done. It was pointed out, for example, that the U. S. Army tends to exercise a far more stringent intellectual control of research findings than does the U. S. Air Force. As evidence for this, it was stated that SORO generally had fewer "free-wheeling" aspects to its research designs than did RAND (the Air Force-supported research organization). One critic inside SORO went so far as to say that he knew of no SORO research which had a "playful" or unregimented quality, such as one finds at RAND (where for example, computers are used to plan invasions but also to play chess). One staff member said that "the self-conscious seriousness gets to you after a while." "It was all grim stuff," said another.

Another line of criticism was that pressures on the "reformers" (as the men engaged in Camelot research spoke of themselves) to come up with ideas were much stronger than the pressures on the military to actually bring off any policy changes recommended. The social scientists were expected to be social reformers, while the military adjutants were expected to be conservative. It was further felt that the relationship between sponsors and researchers was not one of equals, but rather one of superordinate military needs and subordinate academic roles. On the other hand, some officials were impressed by the disinterestedness of the military and thought that far from exercising undue influence, the Army personnel were loath to offer opinions.

Another objection was that if one had to work on policy matters—if research is to have international ramifications—it might better be conducted under conventional State Department sponsorship. "After all," one man said, "they are at least nominally committed to civilian political norms." In other words, there was a considerable reluctance to believe that the Defense Department, despite its superior organization, greater financial affluence, and executive influence, would actually improve upon State Department styles of work, or accept recommendations at variance with Pentagon policies.

There seemed to be few, if any, expressions of disrespect for the intrinsic merit of the work contemplated by Camelot or of disdain for policy-oriented work in general. The scholars engaged in the Camelot effort used two distinct vocabularies. The various Camelot documents reveal a military vocabulary provided with an array of military justifications; often followed (within the same document) by a social science vocabulary offering social science justifications and rationalizations. The dilemma in the Camelot literature from the preliminary report issued in August 1964 until the more advanced document issued in April 1965 is the same: an incomplete amalgamation of the military and sociological vocabularies. (At an early date the project had the code name SPEARPOINT.)

POLICY CONFLICTS OVER CAMELOT

The directors of SORO are concerned that the cancellation of Camelot might mean the end of SORO as well in a wholesale slash of research funds. For while over $1,000,000 was allotted to Camelot each year, the annual budget of SORO, its parent organization, is a good deal less. Although no such action has taken place, SORO's future is being examined. For example, the Senate and House Appropriations Committee blocked a move by the Army to transfer unused Camelot funds to SORO.

However, the end of Project Camelot does not necessarily imply the end of the Special Operations Research Office, nor does it imply an end to research designs which are similar in character to Project Camelot. In fact, the termination of the contract does not even imply an intellectual change of heart on the part of the originating sponsors or key figures of the project.

One of the characteristics of Project Camelot was the number of antagonistic forces it set in motion on grounds of strategy and timing rather than from what may be called considerations of scientific principles.

▪ The State Department grounded its opposition to Camelot on the basis of the ultimate authority it has in the area of foreign affairs. There is no published report showing serious criticism of the projected research itself.

▪ Congressional opposition seemed to be generated by a concern not to rock any foreign alliances, especially in Latin America. Again, there was no statement about the project's scientific or intellectual grounds.

▪ A third group of skeptics, academic social scientists, generally thought that Project Camelot and studies of the processes of revolution and war in general were better left in the control of major university centers, and in this way, kept free of direct military supervision.

▪ The Army, creator of the project, did nothing to contradict McNamara's order canceling Project Camelot. Army influentials did not only feel that they had to execute the Defense Department's orders, but they are traditionally dubious of the value of "software" research to support "hardware" systems.

Let us take a closer look at each of these groups which voiced opposition to Project Camelot. A number of issues did not so much hinge upon, as swim about, Project Camelot. In particular, the "jurisdictional" dispute between Defense and State loomed largest.

STATE VS. DEFENSE. In substance, the debate between the Defense Department and the State Department is not unlike that between electricians and bricklayers in the construction of a new apartment house. What union is responsible for which processes? Less generously, the issue is: who controls what? At the policy level, Camelot was a tool tossed about in a larger power struggle which has been going on in government circles since the end of World War II, when the Defense Department emerged as a competitor for honors as the most powerful bureau of the administrative branch of government.

In some sense, the divisions between Defense and State are outcomes of the rise of ambiguous conflicts such as Korea and Vietnam, in contrast to the more precise and diplomatically controlled "classical" world wars. What are the lines dividing political policy from military posture? Who is the most important representative of the United States abroad: the ambassador or the military attaché in charge of the military mission? When soldiers from foreign lands are sent to the United States for political orientation, should such orientation be within the province of the State Department or of the Defense Department? When undercover activities are conducted, should the direction of such activities belong to military or political authorities? Each of these is a strategic question with little pragmatic or historic precedent. Each of these was entwined in the Project Camelot explosion.

It should be plain therefore that the State Department was not simply responding to the recommendations of Chilean left-wingers in urging the cancellation of Camelot. It merely employed the Chilean hostility to "interventionist" projects as an opportunity to redefine the balance of forces and power with the Defense Department. What is clear from this resistance to such projects is not so much a defense of the sovereignty of the nations where ambassadors are stationed, as it is a contention that conventional political channels are sufficient to yield the information desired or deemed necessary.

CONGRESS. In the main, congressional reaction seems to be that Project Camelot was bad because it rocked the diplomatic boat in a sensitive area. Underlying most congressional criticisms is the plain fact that most congressmen are more sympathetic to State Department control of foreign affairs than they are to Defense Department control. In other words, despite military sponsored world junkets, National Guard and State Guard pressures from the home state, and military training in the backgrounds of many congressmen, the sentiment for political rather than military control is greater. In addition, there is a mounting suspicion in Congress of varying kinds of behavioral science research stemming from hearings into such matters as wire-tapping, uses of lie detectors, and truth-in-packaging.

SOCIAL SCIENTISTS. One reason for the violent response to Project Camelot, especially among Latin American scholars, is its sponsorship by the Department of Defense. The fact is that Latin Americans have become quite accustomed to State Department involvements in the internal affairs of various nations. The Defense Department is a newcomer, a dangerous one, inside the Latin American orbit. The train of thought connected to its activities is in terms of international warfare, spying missions, military manipulations, etc. The State Department, for its part, is often a consultative party to shifts in government, and has played an enormous part in either fending off or bringing about *coups d'état*. This State Department role has by now been accepted and even taken for granted. Not so the Defense Department's role. But it is interesting to conjecture on how matter-of-factly Camelot might have been accepted if it had State Department sponsorship.

Social scientists in the United States have, for the most part, been publicly silent on the matter of Camelot. The reasons for this are not hard to find. First, many "giants of the field" are involved in government contract work in one capacity or another. And few souls are in a position to tamper with the gods. Second, most information on Project Camelot has thus far been of a newspaper variety; and professional men are not in a habit of criticizing colleagues on the basis of such information. Third, many social scientists doubtless see nothing wrong or immoral in the Project Camelot designs. And they are therefore more likely to be either confused or angered at the Latin American response than at the directors of Project Camelot. (At the time of the blowup, Camelot people spoke about the "Chilean mess" rather than the "Camelot mess.")

The directors of Project Camelot did not "classify" research materials, so that there would be no stigma of secrecy. And they also tried to hire, and even hired away from academic positions, people well known and respected for their independence of mind. The difficulty is that even though the stigma of secrecy was formally erased, it remained in the attitudes of many of the employees and would-be employees of Project Camelot. They unfortunately thought in terms of secrecy, clearance, missions, and the rest of the professional nonsense that so powerfully afflicts the Washington scientific as well as political ambience.

Further, it is apparent that Project Camelot had much greater difficulty hiring a full-time staff of high professional competence, than in getting part-time, summertime, weekend, and sundry assistance. Few established figures in academic life were willing to surrender the advantages of their positions for the risks of the project.

One of the cloudiest aspects to Project Camelot is the role of American University. Its actual supervision of the contract appears to have begun and ended with the 25 per cent overhead on those parts of the contract that a university receives on most federal grants. Thus, while there can be no question as to the "concern and disappointment" of President Hurst R. Anderson of the American University over the demise of Project Camelot, the reasons for this regret do not seem to extend beyond the formal and the financial. No official at American University appears to have been willing to make any statement of responsibility, support, chagrin, opposition, or anything else related to the project. The issues are indeed momentous, and must be faced by all universities at which government-sponsored research is conducted: The amount of control a university has over contract work; the role of university officials in the distribution of funds from grants; the relationships that ought to be established once a grant is issued. There is also a major question concerning project directors: Are they members of the faculty, and if so, do they have necessary teaching responsibilities and opportunities for tenure as do other faculty members.

The difficulty with American University is that it seems to be remarkably unlike other universities in its permissiveness. The Special Operations Research Office received neither guidance nor support from university officials. From the outset, there seems to have been a "gentleman's agreement" not to inquire or interfere in Project Camelot, but simply to serve as some sort of camouflage. If American University were genuinely autonomous it might have been able to lend highly supportive aid to Project Camelot during the crisis months. As it is, American University maintained an official silence which preserved it from more congressional or executive criticism. This points up some serious flaws in its administrative and financial policies.

The relationship of Camelot to SORO represented a similarly muddled organizational picture. The director of Project Camelot was nominally autonomous and in charge of an organization surpassing in size and importance the overall SORO operation. Yet at the critical point the organizational blueprint served to protect SORO and sacrifice what nominally was its limb. That Camelot happened to be a vital organ may have hurt, especially when Congress blocked the transfer of unused Camelot funds to SORO.

MILITARY. Military reaction to the cancellation of Camelot varied. It should be borne in mind that expenditures on Camelot were minimal in the Army's overall budget and most military leaders are skeptical, to begin with, about the worth of social science research. So there was no open protest about the demise of Camelot. Those officers who have a positive attitude toward social science materials, or are themselves trained in the social sciences, were dismayed. Some had hoped to find "software" alternatives to the "hardware systems" approach applied by the Secretary of Defense to every military-political contingency. These officers saw the attack on Camelot as a double attack—on their role as officers and on their professional standards. But the Army was so clearly treading in new waters that it could scarcely jeopardize the entire structure of military research to preserve one project. This very inability or impotence to preserve Camelot—a situation threatening to other governmental contracts with social scientists—no doubt impressed many armed forces officers.

The claim is made by the Camelot staff (and various military aides) that the critics of the project played into the hands of those sections of the military predisposed to veto any social science recommendations. Then why did the military offer such a huge support to a social science project to begin with? Because $6,000,000 is actually a trifling sum for the Army in an age of multibillion-dollar military establishment. The amount is significantly more important for the social sciences, where such contract awards remain relatively scarce. Thus, there were differing perspectives of the importance of Camelot: an Army view which considered the contract as one of several forms of "software" investment; a social science perception of Project Camelot as the equivalent of the Manhattan Project.

WAS PROJECT CAMELOT WORKABLE?

While most public opposition to Project Camelot focused on its strategy and timing, a considerable amount of private opposition centered on more basic, though theoretical, questions: Was Camelot scientifically feasible and ethically correct? No public document or statement contested the possibility that, given the successful completion of the data gathering, Camelot could have, indeed, established basic criteria for measuring the level and potential for internal war in a given nation. Thus, by never challenging the feasibility of the work, the political critics of Project Camelot were providing back-handed compliments to the efficacy of the project.

But much more than political considerations are involved. It is clear that some of the most critical problems presented by Project Camelot are scientific. Although for an extensive analysis of Camelot, the reader would, in fairness, have to be familiar with all of its documents, salient general criticisms can be made without a full reading.

The research design of Camelot was from the outset plagued by ambiguities. It was never quite settled whether the purpose was to study counterinsurgency possibilities, or the revolutionary process. Similarly, it was difficult to determine whether it was to be a study of comparative social structures, a set of case studies of single nations "in depth," or a study of social structure with particular emphasis on the military. In addition, there was a lack of treatment of what indicators were to be used, and whether a given social system in Nation A could be as stable in Nation B.

In one Camelot document there is a general critique of social science for failing to deal with social conflict and social control. While this in itself is admirable, the tenor and context of Camelot's documents make it plain that a "stable society" is considered the norm no less than the desired outcome. The "breakdown of social order" is spoken of accusatively. Stabilizing agencies in developing areas are presumed to be absent. There is no critique of U. S. Army policy in developing areas because the Army is presumed to be a stabilizing agency. The research formulations always assume the legitimacy of Army tasks—"if the US Army is to perform effectively its parts in the US mission of counter-insurgency it must recognize that insurgency represents a breakdown of social order. . . ." But such a proposition has never been doubted—by Army officials or anyone else. The issue is whether such breakdowns are in the nature of the existing system or a product of conspiratorial movements.

The use of hygienic language disguises the anti-revolutionary assumptions under a cloud of powder puff declarations. For example, studies of Paraguay are recommended "because trends in this situation (the Stroessner regime) may also render it 'unique' when analyzed in terms of the transition from 'dictatorship' to political stability." But to speak about changes from dictatorship to stability is an obvious ruse. In this case, it is a tactic to disguise the fact that Paraguay is one of the most vicious, undemocratic (and like most dictatorships, stable) societies in the Western Hemisphere.

These typify the sort of hygienic sociological premises that do not have scientific purposes. They illustrate the confusion of commitments within Project Camelot. Indeed the very absence of emotive words such as revolutionary masses, communism, socialism, and capitalism only serves to intensify the discomfort one must feel on examination of the documents—since the abstract vocabulary disguises, rather than resolves, the problems of international revolution. To have used clearly political rather than military language would not "justify" governmental support. Furthermore, shabby assumptions of academic conventionalism replaced innovative orientations. By adopting a systems approach, the problematic, open-ended aspects of the study of revolutions were largely omitted; and the design of the study became an oppressive curb on the study of the problems inspected.

This points up a critical implication for Camelot (as well as other projects). The importance of the subject being researched does not *per se* determine the importance of the project. A sociology of large-scale relevance and reference is all to the good. It is important that scholars be willing to risk something of their shaky reputations in helping resolve major world social problems. But it is no less urgent that in the process of addressing major problems, the autonomous character of the social science disciplines—their own criteria of worthwhile scholarship—should not be abandoned. Project Camelot lost sight of this "autonomous" social science character.

It never seemed to occur to its personnel to inquire into the desirability for successful revolution. This is just as solid a line of inquiry as the one stressed—the conditions under which revolutionary movements will be able to overthrow a government. Furthermore, they seem not to have thought about inquiring into the role of the United States in these countries. This points up the lack of symmetry. The problem should have been phrased to include the study of "us" as well as "them." It is not possible to make a decent analysis of a situation unless one takes into account the role of all the different people and groups involved in it; and there was no room in the design for such contingency analysis.

In discussing the policy impact on a social science research project, we should not overlook the difference between "contract" work and "grants." Project Camelot commenced with the U. S. Army; that is to say, it was initiated for a practical purpose determined by the client. This differs markedly from the typical academic grant in that its sponsorship had "built-in" ends. The scholar usually *seeks* a grant; in this case the donor, the Army, promoted its own aims. In some measure, the hostility for Project Camelot may be an unconscious reflection of this distinction—a dim feeling that there was something "non-academic," and certainly not disinterested, about Project Camelot, irrespective of the quality of the scholars associated with it.

THE ETHICS OF POLICY RESEARCH

The issue of "scientific rights" versus "social myths" is perennial. Some maintain that the scientist ought not penetrate beyond legally or morally sanctioned limits and others argue that such limits cannot exist for science. In treading on the sensitive issue of national sovereignty, Project Camelot reflects the generalized dilemma. In deference to intelligent researchers, in recognition of them as scholars, they should have been invited by Camelot to air their misgivings and qualms about government (and especially Army sponsored) research—to declare their moral conscience. Instead, they were mistakenly approached as skillful, useful potential employees of a higher body, subject to an authority higher than their scientific calling.

What is central is not the political motives of the sponsor. For social scientists were not being enlisted in an intelligence system for "spying" purposes. But given their professional standing, their great sense of intellectual honor and pride, they could not be "employed" without proper deference for their stature. Professional authority should have prevailed from beginning to end with complete command of the right to thrash out the moral and political dilemmas as researchers saw them. The Army, however respectful and protective of free expression, was "hiring help" and not openly and honestly submitting a problem to the higher professional and scientific authority of social science.

The propriety of the Army to define and delimit all questions, which Camelot should have had a right to examine, was never placed in doubt. This is a tragic precedent; it reflects the arrogance of a consumer of intellectual merchandise. And this relationship of inequality corrupted the lines of authority and profoundly limited the autonomy of the social scientists involved. It became clear that the social scientist savant was not so much functioning as an applied social scientist as he was supplying information to a powerful client.

The question of who sponsors research is not nearly so decisive as the question of ultimate use of such information. The sponsorship of a project, whether by the United States Army or by the Boy Scouts of America, is by itself neither good nor bad. Sponsorship is good or bad only insofar as the intended outcomes can be pre-determined and the parameters of those intended outcomes tailored to the sponsor's expectations. Those social scientists critical of the project never really denied its freedom and independence, but questioned instead the purpose and character of its intended results.

It would be a gross oversimplification, if not an outright error, to assume that the theoretical problems of Project Camelot derive from any reactionary character of the project designers. The director went far and wide to select a group of men for the advisory board, the core planning group, the summer study group, and the various conference groupings, who in fact were more liberal in their orientations than any random sampling of the sociological profession would likely turn up.

However, in nearly every page of the various working papers, there are assertions which clearly derive from American military policy objectives rather than scientific method. The steady assumption that internal warfare is damaging disregards the possibility that a government may not be in a position to take actions either to relieve or improve mass conditions, or that such actions as are contemplated may be more concerned with reducing conflict than with improving conditions. The added statements above the United States Army and its "important mission in the positive and constructive aspects of nation building . . ." assumes the reality of such a function in an utterly unquestioning and unconvincing form. The first rule of the scientific game is not to make assumptions about friends and enemies in such a way as to promote the use of different criteria for the former and the latter.

The story of Project Camelot was not a confrontation of good versus evil. Obviously, not all men behaved with equal fidelity or with equal civility. Some men were weaker than others, some more callous, and some more stupid. But all of this is extrinsic to the heart of the problem of Camelot: What are and are not the legitimate functions of a scientist?

In conclusion, two important points must be clearly kept in mind and clearly apart. First, Project Camelot was intellectually, and from my own perspective, ideologically unsound. However, and more significantly, Camelot was not canceled because of its faulty intellectual approaches. Instead, its cancellation came as an act of government censorship and an expression of the contempt for social science so prevalent among those who need it most. Thus it was political expedience, rather than its lack of scientific merit, that led to the demise of Camelot because it threatened to rock State Department relations with Latin America.

Second, giving the State Department the right to screen and approve government-funded social science research projects on other countries, as the President had ordered, was a supreme act of censorship. Among the agencies that grant funds for such research are the National Institutes of Mental Health, the National Science Foundation, the National Aeronautics and Space Agency, and the Office of Education. Why should the State Department have veto power over the scientific pursuits of men and projects funded by these and other agencies in order to satisfy the policy needs—or policy failures—of the moment? President Johnson's directive was a gross violation of the autonomous nature of science.

We must be careful not to allow social science projects with which we may vociferously disagree on political and ideological grounds to be decimated or dismantled by government fiat. Across the ideological divide is a common social science understanding that the contemporary expression of reason in politics today is applied social science, and that the cancellation of Camelot, however pleasing it may be on political grounds to advocates of a civilian solution to Latin American affairs, represents a decisive setback for social science research.

12

T. R. VALLANCE

The Jousting at Camelot—
or Social Technology
Encounters the Shield
of the Social Structure

Professor Theodore Vallance of the Pennsylvania State University was the director of the Special Operations Research Organization (SORO) during the Camelot affair described in the previous chapter.

In the invited piece which follows, Professor Vallance discusses why Camelot may have been ahead of time.

Many things have been written about a once and future research adventure that bore the shorthand label of Project Camelot. Some of these writings were attempts at accurate reporting of a large and complex research experience, some were selective in illustrating problems in conducting large-scale social science, and some appeared as therapeutic experiences for their writers. Readers unacquainted with the project should see the short summary article that is reprinted on the pages following this note.[1]

Out of an experience having the scope and complexity of Project Camelot—including its gradual inception, rapid rise, and sudden demise, the interested observer could not fail to learn many things—and indeed many of these learnings have already been extensively recorded. However, many of the facts remain yet unrecorded, and some of the lessons are yet to be learned. It would have been interesting and valuable, even though impossible, to have had an accurate accounting of all of the events and the perceptions of events that made up "the Camelot affair" in its entirety. So many of the questions that were asked, the charges that were made, the motives that were imputed—not to mention the mere facts of the affair— would, if recorded in clear relation to one another, have given the social science and policy study communities some valuable lessons in how and how not to plan, coordinate, conduct, and report broad-scale social science on matters of political, bureaucratic, and emotional concern and sensitivity. But, alas, this was not done.

The Camelot affair continues to survive as a legend in the Washington foreign service bureaucracies and in parts of academe. Were there certain unique features of that project that served to generate so much concern? Were there conditions inside the federal foreign relations and defense research hierarchies such that nearly any major social science research project would spark controversy? Were social scientists in the Defense Department really (inadvertently or otherwise) on the verge of becoming dominant in foreign policy making? And were the "official" holders of the policy making charter in the State Department truly being outdistanced by what they perceived to be more aggressive and quantitatively oriented social scientists from Defense? Were the sponsors, managers, and scientists of Project Camelot naive in expecting less of an outburst from sensitive politicians and from politically alert social scientists in Latin America? Why were American social scientists who were not a part of the project—and who therefore had rather incomplete knowledge about it—so ready to criticize and condemn, or (in smaller numbers) so ready to praise and defend, the objectives and methodology of this large-scale piece of social science? The fact that such questions continue to be discussed suggests that "big social science," to use Gabriel Almond's term, especially as illustrated by Project Camelot was ahead of time.

The following paragraphs are intended to suggest what being ahead of time might mean for social science, and how the elements of such a meaning might be revealed in the events of the Camelot controversy.

In essence, I suggest that social science has developed a set of supporting technologies which when rightly used under ideal conditions are capable of producing data of high reliability, of generating hypotheses and testing them with quite satisfactory precision; but there are, however, many conditions that make up the environment of social science that render these technologies weak and imprecise and on occasion make them politically hazardous and perhaps even unethical, depending on the reference frame of him who would set ethical standards. Or to put it another way: The technologies of theory building, hypothesis formulation, systems simulation, experimental design, project planning and administration, statistical analysis, and the rest of the equipment of social science, while excellent in many respects, are yet incomplete in their detailed development. The result is that the applied technology of conducting social science is yet likely to encounter unexpected obstacles, to arouse unwanted and often unwarranted suspicions, to appear or to be threatening to established institutions and values, and thus to surprise and disappoint its practitioners, dismay its sponsors, and fail in its objectives.

Social science—whether basic or applied, whether hypothesis testing or change making in intent—is usually conducted in a setting which includes the behavior of people living in social systems. These systems have value—positive or negative—for the people involved in or tangential to them. The scientific experiment requires change and its measurement. Thus the scientifically valid measurement by itself is value implicative quite independently of changeful purposes, for it typically enters the privacy of people and suggests the possibility and desirability of things being different from what they now are—and this can be threatening. Social science, whether the most theoretical and basic or clearly operational and applied, is value relevant—from hypothesis to data collection and reporting—and carries with it the risk of error, objection, and failure generated from and in the reactions of the people being studied.

In the Camelot case, this problem showed itself in several ways:

1. Within the American social sciences family there was anxiety over the impending competition for talent and for access to societies that were to be studied. Even in 1965 there were concerns about oversaturating some Latin American countries with North American pollsters and biographers of the elites. A past president of the American Political Science Association told me clearly that Camelot would encounter recruiting problems as a defensive reaction from people already in the business. The structure of domestic social science was thus reactively engaged.

2. Several staff members of the State Department showed lukewarm official and cool private reactions to the prospect of a major research project with clear foreign policy implications being funded by the Defense establishment. Empirical social science was on the march and directly into the territory long guarded as its own by more intuitively guided policy makers; the ambitious scope of Project Camelot raised anxieties already well formed. The structure of domestic policy-making structures was thus also engaged.

3. In Chile a group of social scientists holding skeptical attitudes toward the United States reacted—and with considerable outrage—to partial knowledge of the project, especially when the purveyor of such knowledge needlessly and unsuccessfully tired to conceal its Army sponsorship. Their feelings were magnified several times over by anti-U.S. political groups.

Some American social scientists had earlier expressed concern over the sponsorship of the project by a military arm of the U. S. Government and argued that sponsorship and management by a non-operational agency such as the Smithsonian Institution would be less likely to provide nervous reactions within foreign countries. This concern turned out to be well founded, for misinformation imparted in Chile about the nature of the project was given a basis for exaggeration in the fact that the work was being conducted by a prime contractor of the U. S. Army. But any operational foreign policy arm of the U. S. Government might not have come off better under the circumstances. Thus was the structure of nationalist attitudes reactively engaged.

One thing that is needed, it seems, in order to successfully pursue extensive social science projects is an improved understanding of the processes and technologies of social change—for large social science implies and creates social change, whether by intention or by accident. Though there is an encouraging growth of interest in social change as a field of specialization among behavioral scientists, we are far removed from having such knowledge readily available in handy manual form. Short of this, each project of significant magnitude should build into its operational plans a component of analysis of the project itself.

Each element of a large social science project should be looked at with this general question in mind: How will the people being studied see this part of the project as bearing on their personal and institutional values and how will they react to it? Responses to this question and its variants will then provide guidance to setting up the techniques of data collection, including not only interview methods, but the timing, the rate of collecting data, and sample designs. And they may also suggest revisions in the hypotheses themselves, especially if the constraints on data collection should result in a logical structure and quality of data that could not support the original aims. Thus, because social sciencing itself produces change, quite apart from any subsequent actions toward change which might come as a result of the research, he who would practice "big social science" would be well advised to do a "systems analysis" of the project he would set up.

It would doubtless be of much value to social science to have each major project incorporate a plan to systematically record and analyze the processes of the project itself—including not only the research techniques but extending to implicated agencies and populations. Through a series of such case studies, especially if they could be accommodated to a fairly standard methodology, much could be learned about the social science of social sciencing, with some advances in the study of social change coming along as a fringe benefit.

Was this being done in the course of Project Camelot? Yes, but not even the wisdom of hindsight can say that its intensiveness would have been adequate to the requirements of the project.

Another way of dealing with the problem of social impact of the activities of large social science projects is to forgo establishing a project as a unified management entity, and instead to attempt to pursue the same ends by way of smaller projects diversely administered but integrated by a master plan. If the major advantages of unification—integrated planning, correlated timing, good internal communication—could be realized through such a procedure, its own advantages of lesser overall visibility and greater ease of involvement of diverse university resources might prevail over the higher management costs sure to ensue. But then it would be a different project, I believe, because the big *if* could probably not be effectively brought about, given the nature of American academicians and their institutions.

Another aspect of prematurity—being ahead of time—that is illustrated in Project Camelot is the imperfection of systems for maintaining effective communication and cooperative relations among the institutions and people that are required for the successful practice of big social science. Complex projects require that many skills, residing in the separate heads of differently trained people whose academic and institutional loyalties are also different, somehow be orchestrated. Honest commitment to a broad objective—for example fostering social and economic development in X, Y, and Z countries—when pursued toward the operational nuts and bolts of selecting societal models, defining variables to be measured, designing surveys, awarding subcontracts, giving credit, acknowledging influence and intellectual obligation—all of these inevitably uncover and generate different viewpoints, needs for compromise, personality clashes, and the like. Much time is needed to identify these things clearly and to work out the operating problems.

Plans for large projects cannot be successfully laid in the climate of urgencies often set by the needs of bureaucrats to make their marks before being rotated to other positions or to meet the arbitrary features of a government budgeting cycle. Problems of this sort arose during the Camelot period and probably played some part in the controversy—for the speed with which the plan was developed undoubtedly permitted some misunderstandings to persist about the nature and objectives of the program. And we may never know for sure what role the interdepartmental rivalries within the federal establishment played in bringing the work to its sudden close.

Just what is it, then, that is ahead of time in social science? Is it the methodology and the associated technologies? Or is it the social conscience, the ambitions or the institutionalized scentific values of the social scientist—ever eager to understand the human condition and possibly to improve it, yet still unprepared to apply his skills in full understanding of the applied science of social science?

I think it is the methodology, the logical structure, the assortment of techniques and tools that have outrun the social scientist's understanding of the very content of his subject matter —of social change, of conflict, of bureaucratic and other institutionally based attitudes, of the workings of the human emotions of love, jealousy, hope, greed, generosity, and commitment.

Thus, as we grow in our understanding of human behavior— especially of behavior in the complex structures of human society—we shall come also to a more effective technology of social research. Then can human understanding of humanity grow apace.

And to what ends?

But that is another story.

REFERENCES

1. Irving Horowitz's collection of readings *The Rise and Fall of Project Camelot* (MIT Press, 1967) will supply the interested reader with further details of fact, opinion, and fantasy. "Technical Information of Congress," a recent report to the Subcommittee on Science, Research, and Development of the House Committee on Science and Astronautics prepared by the Legislative Reference Service of the Library of Congress, discusses the project in the context of science policy issues raised by it. (U. S. Government Printing Office, Apr. 1969.)

13

P. M. BOFFEY

Ovshinsky: Promoter or Persecuted Genius?

How can we tell if a new discovery is a real addition to our store of knowledge—or if it is completely false? Mesmer's theory of "animal magnetism" was accepted by scientists and public alike and his cures were internationally acclaimed: We know now that the entire thing was a hoax. On the other hand we accept Semmelweis as a benefactor of mankind for his fight to eliminate childbed fever, although he died a broken man because his work was scorned and rejected during his lifetime. From our privileged historical viewpoint we can see the immeasurable differences between these two men and scoff at those who could not see the truth at the time, forgetting that it is only the perspective of history that enables us to be correct now. Would our judgment have been so secure if we had been living at the time these events occurred? Can we be as objective about discoveries being made today—even with the wealth of technical knowledge at our disposal? Is Stanford Ovshinsky, the controversial center of the following chapter, the discoverer of a new physical principle or a con-man? This article about him appeared in the August 15, 1969, issue of Science.

Last November an inventor-scientist-entrepreneur from Michigan gained national headlines with the announcement of a "scientific discovery" that he predicted would revolutionize solid-state physics and electronics. The inventor was Stanford R. Ovshinsky, a self-educated high school graduate who heads Energy Conversion Devices Inc., a tiny profitless electronics company in suburban Troy, Michigan, about fifteen miles from downtown Detroit. His "discovery" involved the detection of unusual electrical switching effects in amorphous, or glassy, materials and the production of new electronic switching devices from these materials.

In a press release dated November 11, 1968, Ovshinsky's firm triumphantly announced that this "new and completely unexpected phenomenon" was expected to "transform the electronics industry much as the transistor did 20 years ago." Among the marvels promised were large, flat television displays that could be hung on the wall like pictures; pocket-sized computers; and missile guidance systems which would be impervious to radiation.

PRAISED AND DENOUNCED

The immediate reaction to Ovshinsky's announcement ranged from extravagant enthusiasm to bitter denunciation. On the one hand, some of the world's leading solid-state physicists were quoted as hailing the dawn of a new age. Sir Neville Mott, director of the Cavendish Laboratory at Cambridge University in England, who is an unpaid consultant to Energy Conversion Devices (ECD), called Ovshinsky's work "the newest, the biggest, the most exciting discovery in solid-state physics at the moment," according to a report in the New York *Times*. Similarly, Morrel H. Cohen, director of the James Franck Institute at the University of Chicago, predicted that "discovery of the Ovshinsky effect is going to have the same kind of impact on fundamental physics the transistor had." Cohen is a paid consultant and a stockholder in the company.

On the other hand, many of the nation's leading electronics companies pooh-poohed the importance of Ovshinsky's announcement, claiming that the switching effect supposedly discovered by Ovshinsky had been known for years and showed little promise of leading to the production of practical semiconductor devices. Among the giants of American industry that were quoted as throwing cold water on Ovshinsky's supposed breakthrough were Bell Telephone Laboratories, International Telephone and Telegraph, Raytheon, and Texas Instruments.

Energy Conversion predicted that its devices—although not directly comparable to transistors in all respects—would make possible "smaller, faster, simpler, more reliable, and much cheaper electronic circuitry than is possible with transistors." The devices can also handle alternating current—a feat which is clumsy with transistors—and they are more resistant to nuclear radiation than conventional semiconductor devices, an asset which may prove useful in space and military applications. However, critics complained that the devices are unreliable, unstable, and hard to reproduce.

Ovshinsky said he had developed two basic switches to control current flow in solid-state circuits. Neither device is available commercially, but both are being produced in small quantities at Energy Conversion.

One device, which Ovshinsky calls the Ovonic Threshold Switch, acts as an insulator and blocks current until a voltage of just the right threshold is applied, at which point it suddenly becomes a conductor and passes current. The device continues to pass current as long as the required voltage is applied, but when the voltage drops below a critical value, the device again goes into the blocking state. The other device, which Ovshinsky calls the Ovonic Memory Switch, also switches from blocking to conducting when a threshold voltage is applied, but it then remains in the conducting state even when the current is turned off; a pulse of current must be applied to convert it back to the blocking state. The device thus has a "memory" of the last state it was in. The threshold switching phenomenon that occurs in both devices has been dubbed the "Ovshinsky effect" by Ovskinsky and his scientific colleagues (but not, it must be emphasized, by his legion of critics).

Ovshinsky's claims caused quite a stir largely because his devices seemed to pose a challenge—some would say "threat"— to existing solid-state theory and technology. Solid-state electronics has thus far concerned itself primarily with crystals— that is, materials which have a regular, periodic atomic structure —and with minor imperfections in these crystals. Conventional semiconductor devices such as the transistor, for example, are made from carefully grown crystals that are "doped" with very precise amounts of impurities to enhance their electrical qualities. Ovshinksy's devices, on the other hand, are made from glassy materials that have a disordered atomic structure, and the amount of impurity in these materials does not seem to matter very much. A challenge was thus posed on two levels. Could solid-state theorists explain how the switching effect worked in these "messy" disordered materials? And could these materials actually be made into practical semiconductor devices that might compete with existing technologies?

INTERIM ASSESSMENT

Nine months have now passed since Ovshinsky's dramatic announcement, and while it is still too early to assess fully the importance of his contribution, it has become clear that (i) Ovshinsky, though he never went to college, is an unusually bright individual who is apparently able to break out of traditional ways of thinking; (ii) he is also a zealous promoter who has a knack for collecting eminent scientific advisers and then using them to gain recognition from the public and the scientific community; (iii) Ovshinsky's scientific contributions, and his promotional methods, remain matters of great controversy in the physics fraternity; nevertheless, (iv) Ovshinsky has sparked intense interest in the field of amorphous semiconductors at a time when solid-state physics, according to some of its most eminent practitioners, was becoming dull and predictable.

Whether another technological revolution is indeed around the corner remains to be seen. But it is interesting to note that over the past 9 months some eminent scientists have retreated from the extreme positions they were previously identified with. Mott, whose dramatic quote in the New York *Times* was picked up and repeated by many other publications, denies ever making the statement attributed to him. "That's not the kind of language I used, or would use," he told *Science* in a trans-Atlantic telephone interview. "I think I may have said it was a very interesting development. I guess the reporter just decided to put it in good old Americanese." Mott said he thinks Ovshinsky's switching devices are "of very considerable interest" and "worthy of further experimental investigation," but he added that "only the future can tell if the devices will be technologically important—I would not stick my neck out on that." (However, William K. Stevens, the *Times* reporter who interviewed Mott, says there is "no question that Mott made the statement. I had a good telephone connection and I took it down on my typewriter.")

There has been a similar retreat by some scientists who were initially harsh in their judgment of Ovshinsky. Benjamin Lax, head of the National Magnet Laboratory at M.I.T., told *Science* he was originally skeptical of Ovshinsky's claims and remains skeptical, feeling Ovshinsky's devices have been "oversold in the press" and have "not yet proved themselves." But Lax notes that Julius Feinleib, one of the brightest young physicists at M.I.T.'s Lincoln Lab, will soon join Ovshinsky's company for a year, and he comments: "If Feinleib's willing to devote his time to this, there may be something in it. Let's wait and see. We've all been wrong before."

INDUSTRY INTEREST

Most of the negative comments about Ovshinsky's devices have come from companies that might be considered competitors of Ovshinsky's. In contrast, some big companies that are potential "users" of the new technology have recently expressed sympathetic interest. A Xerox vice-president has called the materials "very promising." Zenith Radio's vice-president for research, Robert Adler, told *Science* he is watching Ovshinsky's work "with great interest." And the top scientist at a computer manufacturer confided: "It may not be the greatest thing since sliced bread, but there's enough in it to warrant careful examination by people like ourselves. There may be applications that haven't even appeared yet."

One of the most notable developments of the past 9 months has been a sharp upsurge of interest in amorphous materials among solid-state physicists. In March, a symposium sponsored by IBM and the American Physical Society included two papers relating to amorphous semiconductor switches, one emanating from Bell Telephone Laboratories and one from Energy Conversion. According to Marshall I. Nathan, of IBM, these two papers "provoked the most spirited discussion of the conference." A few days later, at the American Physical Society's annual meeting in Philadelphia, Energy Conversion scientists spoke to a crowd of perhaps one thousand. Then, in May, some three hundred participants attended a four-day symposium in New York City—sponsored by the Picatinny Arsenal and the Army Research Office-Durham—that was devoted entirely to semiconductor effects in amorphous solids. The symposium was remarkable, according to some participants, both for its large attendance and for its highly polarized, emotionally charged atmosphere.

"It was very hard to remain neutral," says David Adler, associate professor of electrical engineering at M.I.T., who has recently become a consultant to Ovshinsky's firm. "It was like a basketball game. People were cheering on one side and booing on the other. I never saw anything like it at a scientific meeting before."

The meeting produced several sharp personal exchanges. In one instance, a General Electric scientist showed slides of Ovshinsky's newspaper publicity and made it clear he didn't intend to discuss science in such a flamboyant fashion. That won appreciative laughter from part of the audience, but brought a lofty retort from one of Ovshinsky's scientific backers deploring the introduction of personal innuendo into a professional meeting. In another instance, a Texas Instruments scientist gave a paper raising questions about Ovshinsky's work, and Ovshinsky later ran up, grabbed the microphone, and described his detractor's work as "crap." That gave the anti-Ovshinsky forces an opportunity to regain the high road, and a Bell Laboratories scientist piously observed that the word "crap" had no place in a technical discussion. Several participants have told *Science* these exchanges were "unbelievable" and "in poor taste," but there is no doubt that they provide an accurate reflection of the intense feelings that Ovshinsky arouses among physicists.

Last month Ovshinsky delivered a paper at the prestigious Gordon conferences in New Hampshire, and next month Mott is hosting an international symposium on non-crystalline materials in England, so there is no question that amorphous semiconductors have become a matter of great interest in the international physics community. This interest has been building up for years and is not, of course, due solely to Ovshinsky. But even Ovshinsky's detractors are inclined to credit him with a major role in dramatizing the importance of amorphous materials.

THE MAN AND HIS BACKGROUND

Opinion is sharply divided as to what sort of a man Ovshinsky is. His critics generally picture him as a glib con-man and promoter. His supporters picture him as an oppressed genius who is being persecuted by the forces of status quo in industry and science. As is usual in such cases of controversy, there seems to be an element of truth in both pictures.

Ovshinsky has already experienced something of an Horatio Alger climb to prominence. He was born into a poor family forty-six years ago in Akron, Ohio. His father, an immigrant Lithuanian Jew, scratched out a living chiefly by collecting junk and then selling it. Ovshinsky himself dropped his formal education in 1941 after simultaneously graduating from high school and from night trade school. "School bored me," he says. "I didn't find it pertinent to the world."

Leaving school seems not to have slowed Ovshinsky's intellectual development in the least. Indeed, Hellmut Fritzsche, a University of Chicago physicist who is a vice-president of Energy Conversion, theorizes that Ovshinsky may have been lucky to avoid the conventional crystal-oriented instruction dished out to solid-state physicists in the universities, for he was thus presumably better able to appreciate the possibilities of amorphous materials. At any rate, Ovshinsky has continued to educate himself broadly and deeply by reading and experimenting on his own, and he has not confined himself to physics. Sir Neville Mott finds Ovshinsky "both charming and extremely cultured—a man of very, very wide interests. I noticed on his bookshelf a German playwright (Ernst Toller) that I had read with enthusiasm years ago. I've never met anyone else who has read him."

Ovshinsky has more than once surprised the experts by educating himself in a highly technical field and then offering new insights.

In 1955, Ernest Gardner, then chairman of the anatomy department at Wayne State University's medical school, received a letter in the mail containing an unsolicited manuscript from Ovshinsky. The paper suggested mathematical models that might explain how the nervous system functions and indicated that Ovshinsky had read extensively in the biomedical literature. "We were intrigued," recalls Gardner, who is now dean of the medical school. "A number of things in the paper revealed inexperience but reflected intelligence and imagination." Ovshinsky was invited to test out some of his ideas experimentally at the medical school, and his name appears as a junior author on several papers published by the medical school's researchers in the late 1950s. Gardner recalls that Ovshinsky "brought an attitude toward the work that was a little bit different. He would raise questions that made you stop and think about things you usually take for granted." Ovshinsky was also the sole author of three papers on schizophrenia (published in the *Journal of Nervous and Mental Disease* and the *Journal of Neuropsychiatry*), and he gave a talk on the physical basis of intelligence to the Detroit Physiological Society in 1959. Ovshinsky says his interest in how nerve cells store and switch information led directly to his search for switching effects in amorphous materials, and he intends ultimately to return to his neurophysiological studies, believing in "the unity of science."

Ovshinksy's business career has been highlighted by numerous inventions and the founding of small companies to exploit these inventions. After graduating from high school in 1941, Ovshinsky worked as a machinist for a few years, then ran his own shop for a while. In 1946, he founded a small manufacturing company to exploit a new metal-cutting machine he had invented. Four years later, lacking financial backing, he liquidated the company and sold patent rights on the machine to a Connecticut firm. After working for others for five years—first for the Connecticut firm, then as director of research for the Hupp Corporation—he again ventured out on his own, in 1955, and founded a tiny company to serve as a vehicle for his work on new types of electrical controls for automatic equipment. Three years later he sold his invention of an electrochemical switching device based upon amorphous oxides to another small company, and became president of, though not the chief power in, that company. In 1960, he left to found Energy Conversion. Through it all, Ovshinsky has kept the Patent Office busy. He has been issued at least thirty-eight patents on various machine tool and electrical inventions.

Energy Conversion started in a storefront, with Ovshinsky, his wife, and children serving as work force. Today it occupies two modest one-story buildings and has a staff of about one hundred. As might be expected for a firm trying to develop a new technology, Energy Conversion has lost money every year but one. In fiscal 1968, it showed a net loss of $714,210 and in fiscal 1969 reported losses are running about the same. Most of the expenditures are going for product development, research, and patents. Capital has come from private investors, a public stock offering, licensing agreements, and a few government contracts. Energy Conversion currently has four military contracts, and Ovshinsky is said to be pressing for more. Well-placed sources report that one of Ovshinsky's financial backers, exerting pressure through an influential U.S. senator, recently arranged a meeting between Ovshinsky and John S. Foster, Jr., the Pentagon's research chief. Ovshinsky's pitch: He's being penned in by entrenched industry and needs government funding to break through the blockade.

Ovshinsky seems well off in terms of personal finances. He and his second wife, Iris, who holds a doctorate in biochemistry and serves as vice-president and treasurer of Energy Conversion, received a combined compensation of about $50,000 from the company last year. They also own stock which had a paper value of about $18 million at the end of last week. If the company should fail, the stock would not be worth much, but if it succeeds, Ovshinsky will clearly be a multimillionaire.

Perhaps the most striking feature of the company is its formidable array of scientific talent. When Ovshinsky decided he needed help in explaining the switching effect in the early 1960s, he first called John Bardeen, winner of a Nobel Prize for his work on transistors. (Bardeen, incidentally, feels Ovshinsky's work is "very interesting scientifically, but the practical applications are still uncertain.") Bardeen was too busy and suggested Fritzsche instead. Fritzsche became excited over the potential and signed on as a consultant in 1963, becoming a vice-president in 1965. Ovshinsky next latched onto Nobelist I. I. Rabi who came out to look over the company on behalf of a group of investors and was persuaded to serve, first as a director, and now as a consultant. Over the past few years Ovshinsky seems to have filled his consulting stable with a good portion of the leading researchers in relevant fields. He now has eleven consultants, including such renowned figures as Morrel Cohen, of Chicago, and David Turnbull, of Harvard.* Most receive consulting fees, but Cohen and Fritzsche own stock as well. In recent months, Ovshinsky has been recruiting full-time researchers. By this fall he will have five full-timers on the scene.†

CONTROVERSY OVER STYLE

Much of the criticism directed at Ovshinsky stems from a distaste for his style of operating. Questions have been raised about the way he got his paper published in *Physical Review Letters,* about the press conference he staged last November, about the way in which he has gained recognition with the help of his eminent scientific backers, and about gyrations in the company's stock. There is sharp disagreement over whether Ovshinsky should be praised or blamed for his behavior—but whatever one thinks of the matter, it is interesting to note that Ovshinsky's stable of eminent scientists has played a major —perhaps crucial—role in bringing him to prominence.

Prior to last fall, Ovshinsky had gained greater recognition abroad than he had in this country. His first major scientific talks were given in the Soviet Union and in Rumania in 1967. And last year he was awarded the Diesel Gold Medal of the German Inventors Association "in recognition of his discovery of the semiconductor switching effect in disordered and amorphous materials." Ovshinsky says he was nominated for the award by the research director of a leading German electronics firm who had visited his plant. Only three other Americans

* Other consultants, in addition to Cohen, Fritzsche, Mott, Rabi, and Turnbull, include David Adler, M.I.T.; Arthur I. Bienonstock and Richard Bube, Stanford; Karl W. Boer, Delaware; Heinz K. Henisch, Penn State; and William Paul, Harvard.

† Edward Fagen, originally at the University of Pittsburgh; Julius Feinleib, M.I.T.; John de Neufville, a new Harvard doctorate; Robert F. Shaw, Cavendish Laboratory, Cambridge; and James Thompson, University of Texas.

have won the award: Nobel laureate John Enders, Wernher von Braun, and Edwin Land.

The event which made possible Ovshinsky's jump into national prominence was his publication of a paper in the November 11, 1968, *issue of Physical Review Letters,* a prestigious journal of the American Physical Society. The paper was rejected at one point on the ground that it was more suitable for an applied physics journal, but it was ultimately published after two of Ovshinsky's most prominent scientific associates—namely Fritzsche and Turnbull—wrote letters arguing that Ovshinsky's work was of great interest to the international physics community. Ovshinsky's critics complain that he "pulled strings" to get his paper published in a leading journal. They contend that *Physical Review Letters* is supposed to carry "hot" items of a "basic" scientific nature whereas Ovshinskys work, which had been described to some extent in magazine advertisements over the years, was "old stuff" of an "applied" nature. Kasturi L. Chopra, author of a book on thin film phenomena, charged publicly that Ovshinsky's article constituted "a sad example of the misuse of a scientific journal for commercial publicity." He said Ovshinsky's discussion of the switching phenomenon "is not new and is in fact borrowed piece by piece from various references." Ovshinsky's backers tend to dismiss such criticisms by noting that Ovshinsky's work has, in fact, generated considerable interest among physicists. They regard the intervention of Fritzsche and Turnbull as less a case of "pulling strings" than of "righting a wrong." In an effort to counter persistent complaints, the editors of *Physical Review Letters* explained their decision to publish Ovshinsky's paper in the March issue of *Physics Today,* then explained their explanation in the July issue of the same magazine.

Probably no aspect of Ovshinsky's work has so angered critics as the tremendous newspaper publicity he received at the time his paper was published last fall. Without question the publicity would have been more restrained were it not for the enthusiastic endorsements Ovshinsky received from his scientific backers and the publication of his paper in a leading journal.

Shortly before the paper was scheduled to appear, Energy Conversion held an advance briefing for leading science reporters at its Michigan plant. Ovshinsky, Cohen, and Fritzsche all gave talks, and the reporters were given a press release prepared by John Osmundsen, a former New York *Times* science writer who had been employed by Ovshinsky to handle press relations.

The press conference resulted in a barrage of favorable articles. Ovshinsky's work was highlighted in page-one stories in the New York *Times*, Washington *Post,* and other leading papers, as well as in a major article in the financially influential *Wall Street Journal.* A Detroit *News* headline even nominated Ovshinsky for a Nobel Prize. Some of Ovshinsky's scientific supporters blame the newspapers for running wild with the story, but the newspapers in turn seem to have played the story big largely because of the scientists' endorsements. Stevens, the New York *Times* reporter, says that, had Ovshinsky's work not received enthusiastic comments from such eminent scientists as Cohen, Fritzsche, and Mott, the *Times* "wouldn't have hit the story hard at all—we would have run 500 or 600 words on the business page about another interesting device that may or may not work."

Ovshinsky and his colleagues seem genuinely surprised at the extent of the publicity. They also can't see why their press conference should be considered less respectable than similar press conferences held by other companies and even by university researchers who are announcing a new finding. "It wouldn't have mattered what I did," says Ovshinsky. "They just jumped me, they really jumped me. I became a lightning rod for discontent, jealousy, and commercial rivalries." Still, Energy Conversion was obviously pushing hard for publicity. Writers at the American Institute of Physics report that Osmundsen persistently urged them to put out a press release on Ovshinsky (they didn't). And scientists at Bell Labs report that one of Ovshinsky's scientific consultants called them up and gently chided them for helping to quash the AIP press release (the Bell people say they did no such thing).

STOCK GYRATIONS

The wave of newspaper publicity triggered a dramatic, though temporary, rise in the bid price of Energy Conversion stock—from $57 a share just before the stories appeared to as high as $150 a share immediately afterward. This led to speculation that Ovshinsky may have generated the publicity so as to make an enormous profit selling off shares, but Ovshinsky told *Science* that "no insiders" were involved in the trading. The price later returned to its previous levels. Energy Conversion did sell $2.5 million worth of stock to a private investment group about two weeks after the publicity broke. The price does not seem to have been affected by the publicity (the investors paid $40 a share), but whether the decision to buy was influenced by the publicity is presumably known only to the investors, whose identities have not been divulged.

Much of the criticism of Ovshinsky's "style" comes from well-fed industrial and academic scientists who aren't struggling—as Ovshinsky is—to get a fledgling company established in a field dominated by giant corporations. "The scientific community ought to be taught a little charity," says Robert Adler, vice-president for research at Zenith Radio. "I've met Ovshinsky," he adds. "He's an absolutely first-class promoter and he must hold the world's record for name-dropping. He's used practices that someone working for a big company can afford to frown on. But how the hell are you going to finance something like this unless you're a bit of a promoter?" Many critics also talk as if Ovshinsky had somehow seduced his eminent scientific advisers into serving as unwitting promoters of both him and his company—but the scientists seem genuinely excited and many are far from naive.

The worth of Ovshinsky's scientific contributions is a subject

of bitter dispute. Critics allege that Ovshinsky was not the first
to discover the switching effect and that he therefore has no
right to name it after himself. Actually, the priority question is
extremely muddled, and it is not clear just who deserves credit
for what. Mott, who has a thick file on amorphous semiconductors, says, "Anyone who claims priority is bound to be dis-
puted." Bell Labs and Energy Conversion both hold patents for
switching devices but there is disagreement as to which can
claim the earliest filing date and as to what the patents cover. If
the devices become commercially important, the courts may
have to resolve the issue.

Regardless of who was first, Ovshinsky has clearly done more
work on the devices than anyone else. Bell Labs, after some
initial work in the early 1960s, concluded the devices had little
potential and reduced its efforts—as did a number of other
companies. But Ovshinsky continued to test thousands of amorphous materials in an effort to find the best combinations, and
he seems to be the only one producing devices in a packaged
form. "He has an exceedingly good idea of the chemistry
involved—he's come up with materials that you can work with,"
says Feinleib, the young M.I.T. researcher who is joining Ovshinsky's staff. Morrel Cohen adds: "There are lots of questions
about priority, but the real question is totality of contribution,
and there Ovshinsky's contribution has been the greatest. He's
generated the most excitement and he's got a large and vital
organization devoting its energies to the work. If he hadn't done
it, the others wouldn't be claiming priority."

Where will it all end? The people at Energy Conversion believe they are on the verge of success. They claim many of the
reports of unreliability and instability were caused by mechanical packaging problems, which they have overcome, while
others were caused by the fact that rival investigators didn't
know how to make chemically stable devices. Energy Conversion has been turning out devices in a discrete package and in
thin film form and is now incorporating the devices into actual
products, including electrically alterable "read only" memories

for computers, solid-state electroluminescent displays, and solid-state printers. "We're not just a device company," Ovshinsky says. "We're going flat out to make actual products." Cohen, who says he's "familiar with the problems that stand in the way of a practical technology," adds: "I don't see the need for any breakthrough ideas. I see a need for manpower, time, and money."

Still, there are major hurdles ahead. Even if the company's devices and products work, they may not be outstanding enough to supplant existing products; or they, in turn, may be outmoded by other new technologies before they get off the ground.

Whatever the technological outcome may be, the scientific fallout promises to be substantial. Already scores of physicists are struggling to understand how the switching effect works. There is considerable debate as to whether the phenomenon is primarily electrical or thermal in nature, and there are a number of competing models, none of them generally accepted. Solid-state physics has been gearing up for an assault on disordered systems for several years now, and Ovshinsky seems to have come along at just the right time to dramatize the field. And if his devices ever do catch on, the priority question and the other controversies may no longer seem important. As one eminent scientist observed: "Edison wasn't the first to invent the incandescent bulb but who remembers the guys who preceded him?"

14

M. SINCLAIR

The Strange Case of Polywater

Chemistry might be considered the hardest of the hard sciences with absolute laws, rules, and relationships, the last place where one might expect to find controversy over the nature of a simple substance. However, discovery of what appears to be a new form of water has divided much of the world of chemistry into opposing camps. Is "polywater" a polymer of water, a new molecular form never identified before—or is it ordinary sweat, as reported in early 1971, water with unscientific contaminants and of no special interest? If it is a polymer of water, chemical concepts will have to change and great numbers of established chemists will surely resist this revolution. Many of the reports have been partisan and the arguments heated. However Industrial Research, a journal more interested in the application of technology than the basic theory, has made a brave effort to be impartial in this article by its editor, Michael Sinclair.

Rumblings that a new "anomalous" form of water has been discovered are being felt by chemists the world over. Faint disturbances have been detected by more sensitive surface chemists since 1962 (and even before) but it now is clear that the epicenter of the upheaval in traditional chemical dogma lies in the Soviet Union at the Institute of Physical Chemistry at the Academy of Sciences.

Although most scientists have tried to avoid a direct confrontation, their world is being rocked by a new truth: Water, the substance basic to life itself, may not be quite what most thought it was. Under proper conditions, it becomes something quite different than water.

Now, a second tremor has hit—in the Western Hemisphere this time. It centers on the University of Maryland and the National Bureau of Standards where scientists are reporting that the unusual water discovered by the Russians actually is a polymer, which they have dubbed quite appropriately, polywater.

Significantly, through spectrographic techniques, they have elicited the chemical structure and find that a new type of chemical bond between oxygen and hydrogen never before observed must exist and that this bond presages a whole new class of chemical compounds whose ultimate properties and applications only can be guessed.

At the same time, other chemists, who feel the whole anomalous water issue is a hoax, are preparing evidence to expose the weird water as a silica sol resulting from impurities in the microsamples obtained so far. With revelation of the unusual structure and properties of anomalous water and the mystery surrounding its true identity, researchers in the United States and throughout the world hastily are whipping up fresh batches of the gooey stuff to better categorize, characterize, and classify the new substance. Actually, making anomalous water is quite easy. "You could make it in your basement tonight," quipped one scientist close to a government-funded study of anomalous water. To date, most anomalous water has been formed on the *inside* of freshly drawn quartz and glass capillary tubes. Although capillary tubes are used only because they are "handy containers," they seem to have a magic that few researchers can capture in words. But in a nutshell—they work.

Nor is there any reason for the anomalous water to form only on the inside of the tubes. Although none has yet been reported on the outside, it seems only that it may have been overlooked. Capillaries with inner diameters up to 0.5 mm have been used, but most of the work has been done with capillaries in the 10 to 30 μm range.

The quartz or glass surface, it is reasoned by some researchers, has a catalytic effect on the water molecules condensing on it from the vapor phase. This restructures the water into a different form. Mechanism of the catalysis is not understood, but it will work only with vapor-phase water—it seems to have no effect on liquid water.

Capillaries simply can be suspended over distilled water in an evacuated vacuum desiccator. After about eighteen hours, anomalous water can be found in some of the capillaries. Other methods outlined in Russian research require temperature control to regulate water vapor saturation in the desiccator. The process takes longer, but has more reliable results.

A TIP-OFF AND GASPS OF DISBELIEF

Ironically, the Russian work may actually have its roots in America. In 1928, Dr. Leon Shereshesky, professor of chemistry (now retired) at Howard University in Washington, D.C., noticed that water condensed in small capillaries had a reduced vapor pressure. Toluol, he noted, performed in the same way.

Although he did not continue this work, some U.S. scientists now feel that his observations may have tipped off Dr. Docent N. N. Fedyakin of the Physics Department at the Institute of Light Industry in Kostroma, U.S.S.R., in 1962. He saw something unusual in sealed glass capillaries containing water: Secondary columns formed near both ends of the column of water. These "daughter" columns, which were separate from but grew at the expense of the mother column, had different properties than normal water, Fedyakin deduced.

He then joined eminent surface chemist Dr. Boris Vladimirovich Deryagin, head of the Division of Surface Phenomena at the Institute of Physical Chemistry of the Academy of Sciences. Together they claimed that the daughter columns were ten times more viscous than the mother column and represented a new, "anomalous" form of water.

A cacophony of criticism from fellow scientists who said their observations were caused by impurities or epitaxial rearrangement of the water molecules in the fine 2 to 4 μm diameter capillaries sent them scurrying back to the laboratory to perform the experiments under more rigorous conditions.

This time they found that anomalous water could be formed during condensation of water vapor not only in capillaries, but also on flat and even convex quartz surfaces. The properties they found for anomalous water made even their most liberal colleagues gasp in disbelief. According to Deryagin, the water, in addition to high viscosity and reduced vapor pressure, ranged in density from 1.04 to 1.40 g/cm^3, hardened (not froze) at $-40°$ to $-50°$ C, and would not boil but reverted to normal water vapor at 650° to 700° C. Its index of refraction was 1.48 compared with 1.33 for normal water.

When Deryagin confronted U.S. researchers with his findings at the 1967 Gordon Conference on the Chemistry of Surfaces in June, he was met with skepticism and suspicion. A paper followed in 1968 in *Priroda* (Nature), a Russian journal, but it failed to quiet the critics or supply the needed data to satisfy the quandary—is it a new form of water or just some impurities?

In 1969, a group of British scientists at Unilever Research Laboratories in Port Sunlight, Cheshire, said they had made some anomalous water and basically agreed with the findings of Deryagin. But, because they like the Russians had to work with microgram quantities, obtaining meaningful analytical data to determine structure or identify impurities was almost impossible.

At least one researcher who listened to Deryagin at the Gordon Conference tempered his skepticism with scientific curiosity. A contribution could be made to resolving the anomalous water controversy, reasoned Dr. Robert R. Stromberg, deputy chief of the Polymers Division, Institute for Materials Research at the National Bureau of Standards, if unambiguous spectroscopic and quantitative analysis of the material could be made. He and Dr. Warren H. Grant, staff scientist of the polymer interface section at NBS, set out to make and analyze samples of anomalous water.

At about the same time, an Anglo-American group was looking closely at anomalous water with both infrared and Raman instruments. The team, consisting of Dr. L. J. Bellamy, researcher at the Explosives Research & Development Establishment in England and Dr. Ellis R. Lippincott, professor of chemistry and director of the Center for Materials Research at the University of Maryland (College Park), suggested a possible structure for anomalous water. They felt a tetramer was formed in which the four water molecules form a square by strong hydrogen bonding:

$$
\begin{array}{c}
\text{H} \\
| \\
\text{O—H}\cdots\text{O—H} \\
| \quad\quad : \\
\text{H} \quad\quad \text{H} \\
: \quad\quad | \\
\text{H—O}\cdots\text{H—O} \\
| \\
\text{H}
\end{array}
$$

The freshly drawn silica surface of the capillaries, they noted, could offer a suitable template of this structure. But this notion, for Lippincott at least, was short lived.

This spring, Lippincott and Stromberg, who are old friends, merged their efforts to unravel the mysteries of anomalous water. Lippincott's expertise in diamond research aided the study. A double-beam microscope spectrophotometer capable of ultraviolet, visible, and near-infrared measurements through apertures as small as 10 square microns, used for high-pressure research with diamond pressure cells, contributed to the analysis of the microsamples.

SPECTRUM "DIFFERENT THAN ANY KNOWN SUBSTANCE"

Samples prepared by condensing water vapor on freshly drawn "Pyrex" and fused quartz capillaries were examined in the microscope spectrophotometer. The instrument readout showed that the normal fingerprints had disappeared. In an interview with *Industrial Research*, Lippincott said: "When we took the sample out of the capillary and put it on diamond platelets and ran it on our instrumentation, we immediately got a spectrum that was different from any known substance."

The absence of any water is very striking. "One of the features of this run is the complete absence of OH bands and the appearance of two new bands—one near 1,595 cm^{-1} and an intense doublet in the 1,400 cm^{-1} region," said Stromberg.

Because most of the work in the past had been criticized for inadequate measurement of impurities, the Washington researchers analyzed the material spectrochemically with laser probe excitation and with a copper-spark method. Only trace quantities of cation contaminants were seen. The laser probe is sensitive to 10^{-11}g for certain elements; copper spark is sensitive to 10^{-10}g. Microprobe analysis showed trace quantities of silicon and sodium.

Analysis of the infrared spectral results leads the researchers to believe they have found a new type of chemical bond never seen before. This conviction is bolstered by the results of a computer search of 100,000 infrared spectra through the American Society for Testing & Materials/Dow Chemical Co. SIRCH program—no similar structures were found.

In normal water, the two hydrogens of each molecule are held closely by the oxygen but the molecules are loosely attracted by Van der Waals forces on the order of 4 K cal. In the new type of water, to satisfy their data, Lippincott and Stromberg say there must be a *primary* chemical bond with hydrogen between two oxygen atoms (O-H-O). Although oxygen generally only forms two bonds, this new type of bond apparently allows it to form three linkages.

While the spectra of this new form of water appears to be unique, it does have some striking similarities to chemical systems that have very strong symmetric hydrogen bonds such as those that occur in the bifluoride ion. Because O-H-O is isoelectronic with the bifluoride ion F-H-F⁻, Lippincott and Stromberg feel they can accurately predict the bond lengths and energies.

In *Science*, (Vol. 164, 482–87) they give the O-O distance as about 2.3 angstroms (compared with about 2.8 for normal water). The hydrogen atom is centered between the two oxygens at about 1.5 ang and has a "hydrogen bond" energy of 30 to 50 kcal per bond unit or 60 to 100 kcal per water formula unit. This compares with 119 kcal for the H-OH bond in normal water.

All of this means that the new form of water is held together with much greater force than exists between the molecules of conventional water.

Results of the infrared studies and the Raman work that followed has led the Washington researchers to suggest two different possible structural formulas.

The two polymerlike structures rely on 120-degree bond angles, which would make the structures flat, or 109-degree tetrahedral bonds that would produce a "puckered" structure. These structures definitely are high molecular weight polymers.

The properties that the NBS/UM researchers have attributed to the high polymer form—"polywater"—agree with most of those found earlier by Deryagin. They feel that he was working with dilute mixtures of polywater dissolved in normal water. The highly polymerized water has a narrower density range of 1.39 to 1.40. The decomposition and solidification points, says Lippincott, depend on the degree of polymerization. Figures of as high as 800° C for the former and as low as —80° C for the latter have been mentioned, however.

Contribution of the NBS/UM work, if correct, is significant. It gives researchers a good spectroscopic look at anomalous water. By putting their scientific reputations on the line, the Washington researchers have put anomalous water squarely in the area of "legitimate" chemistry where it will receive close attention from many researchers. If they are right, it could result in a Nobel Prize for Deryagin.

SOME REASONS FOR DOUBT

But the material in the tubes . . . is it *really* a new chemical compound? Some researchers are extremely skeptical, based on their own observations of the surface chemistry of glass and quartz. In their view, Lippincott and Stromberg have failed to prove that silica impurities in the water are not actually at the heart of anomalous water.

A soft-spoken critic is surface chemist Willard D. Bascom at the Chemical Division of the Naval Research Laboratories, Washington, D.C. He sees strong evidence to support his view that polywater is simply a silica sol produced by the corrosive action of small amounts of water on the pristine glass or fused quartz of the freshly-drawn capillaries.

As most surface chemists know, glass and fused quartz have inclusions of alkalies in their surfaces. Small droplets of condensed water will dissolve these alkalies and become extremely corrosive to the glass or quartz surface. By dissolving the surface, silica sols will form. In the case of other chemicals such as alcohols, silica impurities could form silica sol esters.

This may also explain why polywater can be formed only in freshly drawn capillaries and forms faster with Pyrex than fused quartz. Pyrex has more alkali inclusions than quartz and both are extremely reactive with water when freshly formed.

Furthermore, this also may explain why polywater can only be formed from condensed water. Only small quantities of water could reach the degree of alkalinity required to attack the glass or quartz. If the tube were filled with liquid water the dilution would be too great. Once silica is dissolved, however, the concentration required to make a sol is relatively low.

But Bascom is stumped by at least one finding of the NBS/ UM team—if silica sols instead of polywater are in capillaries, why didn't silica show up in the spectra? By analyzing his own anomalous water with an electron microprobe he hopes to conclusively show the composition of the samples. If he sees silica, some of the silica-based models he has developed to fit Lippincott's data may be the answer.

The controversy probably will mushroom as more researchers rush into their labs toting capillaries and vacuum desiccators. Already there are a few interested groups working with the material.

THE CONSISTENCY IS LIKE . . . "VASELINE"

"Polywater is a true polymer of water having a different structure and different bonding than water. The difference between water and polywater is as drastic as the difference between ethylene and polyethylene," says Lippincott.

Once formed, polywater is stable in air. It can be dissolved in water and reconstituted by boiling off the normal water. Like most polymers, polywater produced so far seems to be composed of both high and low molecular weight components. The extent of polymeric properties depends on the extent of polymerization.

Although it so far has only been made in microgram quantities, the high molecular weight components seem to have the consistency, as one researcher puts it, of "Vaseline." You can smear it or poke a hole in it with a wire.

In some forms, it can be evaporated below its decomposition temperature and recondensed as polywater. When heated above the decomposition temperature it recondenses as normal water. Most of the interesting physical properties like strength, optical clarity, lubricity, elasticity, and resistance to various environments will be difficult to test until gram quantities of polywater are available.

At least one group of researchers is interested in that aspect. Dr. Barry Brummer, head, Electrochemistry Department, and Dr. Frank H. Cocks, senior scientist at Tyro Laboratories in Waltham, Massachusetts, have been awarded a $75,000 contract from the Advanced Research Projects Agency of the Department of Defense and a $50,000 contract from the Office of Saline Water to come up with production methods for quantity production of polywater.

Tyro researchers prefer to call polywater ortho water (o-H_2O) and normal water meta water (m-H_2O) to indicate their feeling that polywater is the highest hydrated stable form of water.

Although Brummer would not divulge the approach they are planning to take, they would like to dispense with the capillary tubes, although Brummer admits that a massive capillary tube "farm" may be the quickest way to larger quantities. He would like to produce multigram samples by the end of the year.

The Tyro grants probably represent about half of the government funding in polywater research. At Battelle Memorial Institute, Dr. Harry Goering, assistant manager of technology in the Department of Chemistry, heads up a small, institute-sponsored venture to investigate infrared and nuclear magnetic resonance analysis of polywater as well as preparation. Another group of researchers at Lowell Institute of Technology, Massachusetts, is looking at the basic chemistry involved and possible applications.

APPLICATIONS IN ENGINES AND REACTORS

When discussing potential applications, polywater must be thought of as a new, high-temperature polymer, not simply funny water. As a polymer that seems to be thermally stable, polywater may be useful as a high-temperature fluid. For this reason, it may be attractive as a working fluid in steam engines or as a lubricant in high-temperature environments. An unconfirmed rumor has been circulating, in fact, that William P. Lear, president of Lear Motors Corp. (Reno, Nevada), is developing polywater in a crash program for his new steam autos.

Polywater technology could provide a cheap way to desalt water. The catalytic nucleation of polywater on certain surfaces requires no additional energy and this could be useful in membrane processes for separating pure water from dissolved salts.

Several researchers—including Deryagin and Lippincott—have used deuterium oxide (heavy water) to make polywater. Polyheavywater seems to be just as stable as polywater. Heavy water is used as the moderator in nuclear reactors. In a polywater form, because of the one third greater density of polywater, there would be a higher concentration of deuterium atoms and, hence, less material could be used to get the same moderation. Furthermore, leaks would be much less of a problem because of the high viscosity of the material.

While some researchers are trying to create polywater in their laboratories, others are looking about to see if polywater exists naturally. After all, if polywater is so stable—in fact it may be more thermodynamically stable than normal water—shouldn't we find great gobs of it hanging around?

There is a possibility that intracellular water in living things may have a polywater component. Freeman Cope of the Aerospace Medical Center, Wayminster, Pennsylvania, has probed the electric fields surrounding water molecules inside living tissue using nuclear magnetic resonance and discovered that the water is more like ice than ordinary liquid.

He fed rats on heavy water so that some of their tissue H_2O was replaced by D_2O. Then he examined the deuterium nuclei in their muscles and brains. He interprets the results to mean that much of the water is more ordered than the free liquid.

Another natural source of polywater could be minerals. Lippincott is betting on clay types. "Based on what we know, we feel that certainly this occurs naturally in minerals such as kaolinite and montmorillonites." Water in montmorillonites won't come out until it is heated to 600 to 700° C, which is on the order of temperatures it takes to break up polywater.

Surface chemists have measured the density of the water from some of these minerals and the densities run high too—from 1.2 up to 1.5. Infrared spectra has been prepared, and Lippincott says that these look "suspicious."

Although polywater is stable, it does not nucleate and does not pose the threat to the global water system. As Deryagin pointed out, even if a glass of polywater were poured into the ocean it would be so diluted that not a trace of it would exist.

While this is true on earth, some scientists wonder if the unexpected absence of water vapor in the spectra of the atmosphere of Venus might be caused by a total conversion of Venusian water to polywater.

At this point we have only the barest understanding of polywater. The heyday of new discoveries, new controversies, and perhaps new applications lies closely ahead.

If Deryagin and the NBS/UM researchers are correct in believing they have discovered a new form of water, the most revolutionary and significant discovery will be that a new type of chemical bond has been found. Chemists already are looking at this bond in compounds other than water.

The result could be a whole new class of polymers with properties and applications not known today. At the University of Maryland, work is going on in the formation of polymers of substances containing OH groups such as acetone, methanol, acetic acid, propanol, and amyl alcohol. Researchers are looking closely at the function of the catalyst surface. They are studying metals and other materials to see if they are appropriate nucleation sites.

The chemistry of the OH bond may be in its infancy and may well mature to far eclipse the immediate excitement of polywater.

If Deryagin and those that have followed are proved wrong, the quest for truth will, after all, result in a better understanding of surface chemistry and the universal substance—water.